# The Arctic
# Through Hull's

## By Brian Flaxman

DONATED BY
"STEPHEN H PENN"
"DECKIE LEARNER"
ON THE TRIP WHEN
COLLISION AT ICELAND
TOOK PLACE

"GOOD OLD CHARLIE PITTS"
A GENTLEMAN

# Acknowledgements

Cover painting by Mark Stansfield.

# Introduction

This fact-based book is written by an ex-Hull fisherman. Having worked as a fisherman stood me in good stead for the rest of my life. Fishing is the world's most dangerous occupation, especially if you sail from the port of Hull.

We live and work alongside the bravest and most patriotic men the world has ever seen. We take the good times with the bad times, and we watch as the fishermen's families live their lives in the constant hope their loved ones will come home safely, because no other city in the world has ever built an industry that has lost so many of its people to the sea. It is almost unbelievable that 6,000 Hull men and 900 ships sailed through Hull's St Andrew's sacred lock gates and did not return home. The sacred lock gates are their final place of departure and they hold the spiritual DNA for every single man and ship that ever sailed through them. The city of Hull became known in the fishing communities as the "city of widows".

We watched as the worst storm in living memory raged across Iceland's fishing grounds in full force for fifteen hours, with thirty trawlers listing further over with the weight of up to 20 tons of ice on their structures. Every one of them was in danger of capsizing and sinking.

The Hull trawlers were being lost at sea and the Hull fishermen were being lost with their ships. There were tragedies happening one after the other and the people of Hull were going down on their knees in in grief in the streets, and the St Andrew's dockland is covered in flowers and wreaths.

In 1968, Lilly Bilocca and the ladies of the Fisherman's Charter asked the Hull trawler owners why only the trawlers from Hull were being lost. The owners told the ladies that they had 350 trawlers and 7,000 crewmen working in the Arctic fishing grounds, by far the biggest fleet. There were high-capacity distant sidewinder trawlers in Britain, Europe and the rest of the world and Hull had hundreds more trawlers and thousands more men in its network than the smaller fishing ports. There was more activity, leading to more losses, and those losses were very concerning.

Hull trawlers and the fishermen sometimes had to face the most extreme Arctic weather conditions. In the summer months, the weather around the Arctic fishing grounds can be quite pleasant, with temperatures reaching the 50s, with long hours of daylight and sunshine. But not all the time.

The Fisherman's Charter ladies also asked the trawler owners why they did not pay compensation to the widows of the lost fishermen. The trawler owners told them a fisherman's job is dangerous and, traditionally, it is part of a fisherman's occupation to suffer injury or loss at sea. They were telling us that fishermen were playing a game of chance and knew what they were up against. They said nobody forced them to go to go to sea; they volunteered to do the job and any consequences were put down to 'an act of God'. That was their excuse for not paying out compensation. The trawler owners would not part with one penny, but if you owe them anything, they would take it from you and leave you with nothing. The fishermen in Hull had not had a pay rise for twenty years, while the fish prices and inflation were rising by the day and they knew we had to rely on fishing for our livelihood. They took advantage of this. But what if we all had refused to do the job? These were the kinds of things the people of Hull had to live with from the trawler owners.

Each trawler carried a twenty-man crew, and every trawler weighed between 500 and 700 tons, carrying enough food and water and fuel and up-to-date emergency equipment on their expeditions. They were all self-contained. They were capable of sailing for thousands of miles to any of the Arctic fishing grounds and filling their holds with between 100 to 200 tons of top-quality white fish, getting it back home to the Hull fish market within three weeks.

But sometimes they faced the worst weather conditions and other dangers. There are lots of dangers and hardships trawlermen have to face to earn their living. Hull's fishing network is organised almost to perfection and new trawlers are being built with the latest technology installed. It is important that the fish demand around the country is met, and the Hull fishing community plays a very important part in keeping the network going by working over and above their expectations.

Hull's fishing network was carefully planned by the trawler owners and every Hull trawler carried a twenty-man crew that had the courage to face the dangers on the Arctic expeditions that go hunting for white fish on the Arctic's fishing grounds, including Iceland, Greenland, Bear Island, Spitsbergen, the Barents Sea, the Russian coast, the White Sea, the Norwegian coast and many other places, including the Grand Banks and around Nova Scotia.

**Hull trawlers often challenged the Arctic weather, no matter how bad it got. There were hundreds of fishermen who came to work in Hull, to earn big money, from Grimsby, Fleetwood, North Shields, Lowestoft, Aberdeen, Peterhead and all the Scottish ports. The toughest men from everywhere came to Hull to make up our crews. Sometimes the fish markets and the working community were pushed to their limits to disperse the hundreds of tons of fish from the market to make way for tomorrow's landings, which could be even**

bigger than today's. The city's fishing industry network was huge and created many jobs and businesses for people around the country.

# Chapter 1
# The Arctic Corsair

It's 14 October 1967 and imagine that you are a main character in this book and are on watch with Steve and Dale. You are an experienced fisherman sailing on the Arctic Corsair and you are setting off for Iceland today with the grip of winter coming on. You have said farewell to your friends and family and everyone is upset, with even the dog looking sad. You put on a brave smile, pick up your bag and walk out to the waiting taxi, where some of the crew are waiting for you. The neighbours are watching from behind their twitching curtains and some are talking on their doorsteps, and the kids in the street stop playing and watch you get into the taxi. Your friends, neighbours and family are waving goodbye as your taxi drives away. You start to feel insecure and your nervous channels are sending out messages and you feel sick, but you try to cover it up from your mates, but they have got the nervous channels too; even the most experienced fishermen get the nervous channels and feel sick when they are going away, and again when they are going home, and sometimes at sea if a situation arises.

We drive out of your street onto Hessle Road and see the people going about their daily routines, and you feel like you would swap places with any of them if you could. We turn into West Dock Avenue where Rayners fishermen's pub is on the corner (which will be full to the brim at 11 a.m., as soon as the doors open). We drive under the railway tunnel and to the fish dock.

The taxi drives to St Andrew's dockland and pulls up at the Lord Line quay where the Arctic Corsair is tied up and waiting. It is a nervy feeling and the ship seems to be watching as you get out of the taxi. You climb on board and take your bag into the accommodation where your two watch mates, Steve and Dale, and the rest of the crew, greet you. There are few visitors who are setting us away on board. You go to your berth and put your bags in the bunk. You have to go to the fishermen's store for the things you need for the trip. The store is full of fishermen you know from other ships that are sailing on this tide, and the staff behind the counter are run off their feet. You get what you need and set off back to the Arctic Corsair.

There is a notice on the old pumphouse wall opposite the stores saying that alcohol is prohibited on board trawlers, and offenders will be prosecuted. But nobody reads it, and you go back aboard the Arctic Corsair and have a can and a dram with your mates. Woe betide anyone who upsets us; a man needs a drink in situations like having to leave home and go to the Arctic fishing grounds. If anyone did try to stop us, we would probably refuse to sail, and walk off the ship (the situation never arose).

There is a saying that there is a mountain of empty booze bottles that leads from Hull and Grimsby all the way to Iceland, and it can be seen from space, and the brave men from Hull, Grimsby, Fleetwood, Noth Shields, Lowestoft Aberdeen, and all the Scottish ports, have contributed to it.

The ship's runner is trying his best to get the crew together and is shouting: "Is everyone aboard? Stand by to let go. Everyone ashore who is going ashore." The telegraph rings for stand by, and everyone starts to move and the visitors go ashore. Sometimes there are up to four trawlers tied in a row and you have to climb over them.

We go on deck and let go of the ropes and pull them in. The Arctic Corsair goes astern until she's positioned, then she goes ahead and sails through the sacred lock gates. The visitors wave and shout "All the best" and someone on the quay shouts up at the old man on the bridge, "Bring 'em back alive," to the amusement of the onlookers (comments of this kind are normally accepted). The telegraph rings and the Arctic Corsair's powerful engines spring to life and her screw churns up the water as she picks up speed and pulls away from the lock gates. The old man blows a courtesy cock-a-doodle-doo on the ship's siren that can be heard in the houses and shops and schools on Hessle Road, and sends out a farewell message that the ships are sailing.

You take a long look back at the people on the quay and keep the picture in your mind with a feeling of sadness. Your mind is telling you that you will be home soon. We start the 25-mile journey up the River Humber to the Spurn lightship and into the North Sea. We pass Grimsby's famous tower 13 miles upriver from Hull on our starboard side (the right-hand side). The River Humber is known for its swirling six-knot tides and moving sandbanks and has a reputation for being hard to navigate (you will need a river pilot if you're not familiar with it). The old man and the mate and the third hand are on the bridge until we are clear of the river, and the crew are in their berths sorting their gear, and maybe having a can and a dram to celebrate the voyage ahead.

We approach the Spurn lightship (which is painted red) five miles out to seaward. Ships have to pass her on their red port side (red to red, all is clear go ahead) to prevent collisions. We make a U-turn to port around the Spurn lightship and into the Noth Sea and set a northerly course for Iceland. There is a north-east gale blowing and we are immediately crashing into 40 mph winds on our bow. The engines are straining a changing pitch and the ship shudders and begins to roll, and the smell of diesel and raw veg fills the air and makes your stomach turn. It is 12.30 p.m. and you Steve and Dale are on watch. We are going into heavy seas and have to keep hold of the handrails. Steve holds on to the wheel for support as he steers. Dale is at the radar and the old man is checking his charts and talking to the 'sparks'. He tells us that the automatic steering is broken and it will be out for a few trips while waiting for repair and new parts from Germany, so we will have to steer by hand.

You go down to the accommodation to check around the ship to see if everything is okay. Everyone is in their bunks except for the engineers. The ship is throwing you off your feet and you have to hang on. You have to time your moves. The cook has turned in and there are things banging and rolling about loose and it takes a while to jam things up and check that everything is safe. You come across the galley boy doing his first trip to sea and he is seasick and in a fever, and all he wants to do is to just lie down in the messdeck where he is. He won't get in his bunk, and all you can do is to make sure he is safe and try to reassure him and keep a watch over him. You are satisfied that things are safe and you put your finger through three mug handles of tea and struggle your way back to the bridge.

The bridge is always kept in darkness on a night, for good visibility. You can hear the sparks receiving and sending messages in Morse. You stand at your lookout post on the port wing; it is customary to stand through your watch, to stop you falling asleep on the dark bridge. You tell your watchmates the galley boy is seasick, and he is laid in the messdeck and won't get in his bunk. You say he is not a boy – he is a man. Steve says he's been talking to him, and he's 20 and comes from Manchester and is originally from Caernarfon in Wales.

We talk on the bridge for the rest of our watch and hope the weather is fine in Iceland, and we hope we do a short trip, and about the local gossip and the events we will miss while we are away. We talk in sympathy for the galley boy being seasick. Coming away to sea straight into a force-eight gale on his first trip is a terrible experience. You relieve Steve at the wheel, and the watch passes uneventfully.

It comes to 6 p.m., tea time, and we call the next watch out for tea, and to relieve us. The cook has made a pan of stew (shackles, as we call it), and it is all we can expect, because the weather is too bad for him to cook a meal. The stew is much appreciated, but most of the lads don't turn out for it on the first day, especially if it's bad weather. It's 6.30 and the next watch are on to the bridge to relieve us. It's been a tiring day and we look forward to something to eat and getting out of the way into our bunks.

You, Steve and Dale go down to the messdeck. The cook has coaxed the galley boy into his bunk, and he is in a fever and out of the game. He said if we go into port, he is getting off, and he doesn't care where it is – he will still get off. We are steaming full speed ahead into the wind and getting thrown about in the weather, but the Arctic Corsair will not stop for anything. The galley boy said he didn't expect it to be like this, and he wishes he hadn't come. You tell him he will be okay and will soon get over it.

You and Steve go to your berth, unpack your gear and get into your bunks. You put your back against the bunk side and balance yourself with your knee up against the other side, to stop from rolling about. This is how a fisherman has to sleep. We have all got our own way of doing this and we all find the best individual method. Some of us still sleep like that at home.

The next morning, the wind has dropped. The watch have called all hands out for breakfast, and the old man is having a field day to get the trawl ready before we get to the fishing grounds and to tie it up along the rail ready for shooting. We have to make the most of the fine weather while we have the chance to open the hatches. We heave the nets up onto the deck and stitch them together. We work together as a team and all know what the other is doing. The deckie learner, who is 16 and done four trips to sea, is as hard as nails and fills the net needles. We have a can and a dram and a sing-song to keep us happy while we are working. We usually have a bit of fun on days like this. We all take a case and a bottle away with us and it has usually gone long before we get to the fishing grounds.

The old man and the sparks take the opportunity to dish the bond out while we're all here and make the most of the fine weather too. Cigarettes and tobacco, chocolates and other things are in the bond, but it is cheaper to bring it with you because everything is full price except for cigarettes and tobacco, which are subsidised and cheap. We get a bottle of rum each, which we pay for ourselves, but the old man keeps it locked away and gives it out when it gets cold, a dram at a time. Some skippers abuse it and help themselves to it, and some even help themselves to the co-codamol from the medicine chest too when they feel that way inclined.

We have been working with all hands for six hours, and we have got the trawl alongside and got some other gear ready. We batten the hatches down, and we are all ready for shooting. It's half an hour before dinner time. The cook has made soup, a roast dinner and a sweet.

The galley boy is much better but he's still groggy and unhappy, but he is working and getting fresh air because the doors are open. We ask him why he chose to come to Hull from Manchester, and told us in a distinct Welsh accent that he had heard about Hull's fishermen earning money and it sounded appealing to him. He came in the clothes he stood up in and only had a carrier bag and a few things and that is all he owned. He hitch-hiked down the motorway to Hull and slept in an abandoned car near to the fish dock for three days. He is a character with a likeable, honest, talkative personality and we were amazed at the story he told us.

After dinner, you and Steve and Dale are on watch for six hours until teatime at 6.30 p.m., when you go up to the bridge to relieve the watch. Dale is on the radar. You relieve the man on the wheel, he gives you the course to steer, and you repeat the course after him and this is practised every time the helmsman changes his spell at the wheel. You check the compass to be sure you are steering the right course and check that the rudder indicator is amidships and you observe what is going on ahead and around you. Steve brings you and Dale a drink up to the bridge (tea)!

# Chapter 2

It's 2.15 p.m. on the afternoon of 14 October 1967. We have had a field day with all hands to get the trawl ready for fishing. We are steaming full and we are heading for the Icelandic fishing grounds. You Steve and Dale are on watch. The crew have gone to their bunks and are making the most of their time off before we start fishing. The weather is flat calm with not a breath of wind. The old man has turned in and he's had his fishing jersey washed, thank God.

The sparks is on the bridge and tells us the weather has been good at Iceland, and goes on talking about the cod wars, and how the British fishermen were told to arm themselves with ice axes, and how, as the saying goes, they were told to chop the Icelandic sailors' hands and arms off if they put them on the rail to try to board us. Dale said it's a political dispute and it should be dealt with by the politicians in parliament, and Steve said what if we did chop the Icelandic sailors' hands and arms off, or rammed the gunboat and sank it with all hands, or if they sank us, what would happen then? The sparks said it is not a real war – war was never declared. The politicians are using us to do their dirty work instead of involving the Royal Navy. And what about paying compensation if something bad happened? Would our government pay out and back us up or would they just turn their back on us?

The Icelandic government have got a point when they say to sort it with the British government, because the value of the fish that Hull and Grimsby and Fleetwood are taking from Iceland's waters far exceeds Iceland's economy. Britain is actually stealing part of Iceland's economy. The cod war has ended for now but it still has to be settled with a diplomatic agreement.

Dale says, "Let's have a cup of tea." You go down and check around the ship, The galley boy is peeling potatoes. His name is Ralph. He is still trying to get over his seasickness and has a fever, which is a part of being seasick. He is far from being happy. You tell him he will get over it soon but he is not listening. You make your way back to the bridge and relieve Steve at the wheel.

The sparks comes from the radio room and says there is a fog warning ahead of us. Dale says the visibility is getting poor here. Fog is a nightmare to shipping at sea – it is stressful and exhausting and you strain on your eyes trying to see through it. After a while you start to imagine you have seen something, and you start seeing things that aren't there. The visibility is getting worse by the minute. Dale goes down to tell the old man and comes back to the radar. The old man comes on the bridge almost immediately and stands looking out of the window for a while. We can't see 10 metres ahead of us. The old man rings the telegraph to slow speed and he says this is bad because there is plenty of shipping around here. He opens the windows for us to listen for any warning sirens or bells.

The old man says we have to make headway to get out of the fog because we could sit here for the next two weeks. The windows are open and the cold wind comes rushing around the bridge. The old man gives a prolonged blast on the ship's siren every two minutes. Dale is watching the radar pinging other sips on the screen and he is tracking them, but a radar is not wholly reliable; there might be a radar cluster that gives out false pings and a vessel could get inside them undetected, so we must keep a sharp look out.

The cold starts to get the better of us all and the old man tells you to go down and find some coats and warm clothing and even gloves and hats for us to put on and to bring some tea up after. The sparks has already retreated into his warm radio room and closed the door on us. You go down and get the gear, and the lads are asking what you are doing, and you tell them we are in thick fog and can't see 10 metres in front of us. We've got the bridge windows open and we're frozen stiff. They already knew about the fog because of the telegraph ring and the sirens woke everyone up. Ralph is listening, looking uneasy and trying to weigh the situation up.

After an hour or two on the bridge, it becomes stressful and hard work. The cold starts to set in and, after giving your full concentration for so long, you start imagining things. The old man gives out a prolonged warning blast on the siren then hands the job over to you while he takes a break. He goes to the radio room to see if the coastguard knows how far the fog bank stretches, and there is no end to it for miles ahead of us. We are looking forward to being relieved at teatime because this is very hard and tiring work, but we have to carry on straining our eyes and ears regardless.

Then, suddenly, a siren sounds in the distance and we all confirm we had heard it. The old man blasts out on the siren and Steve rings the bell. Everything goes quiet. We are all listening, watching, and hardly breathing. The other ship's siren blasts out very close now. Too close, and to our horror and surprise, a huge ship's bow looms up out of the fog at ten degrees on our starboard side with the name "Olive" painted on it in big white letters. The old man shouts "Hard to port" but you've already started the manoeuvre by instinct, and then wham, bang, bang, boom. We have collided with a collier and the old man rings the telegraph to stop engines. The lads come running to the bridge and onto the deck to see what is happening. Dale tells them we have collided with another ship, so put some warm clothing and put your life jackets on, and stand by the life rafts waiting for instructions, because we could be holed.

We are in deep shock. It is our worst nightmare. We have been acting with caution and following the rules but it still happened. The sparks is alert and already talking to the coastguard and reporting the incident. The collision impact has already got the lads out and they are on the deck with their life jackets on. The old man tells you and Steve to stay on the bridge with the sparks while he and Dale and the engineers examine the damage. The collier has gone astern into the fog and gone out of vision, but we can hear them sounding their bell. The lads have got the forward hatches open and they have reported water in the hold, and a further inspection confirms we are holed below the waterline and taking in water.

There are some fishing nets to be moved before we can get near the damaged area and they will have to be hoisted onto the deck. The lads waste no time hauling it out with the winch. We have a salvage pump in the engine room and the lads are bringing it along as fast as they can with the engineers following. It takes quite a few attempts to get it started before we begin to pump the water from the hold out onto the deck. But the water is not being pumped from the hold fast enough – the salvage pump cannot cope with the amount of water coming in.

The sparks is speaking to the coastguard and has arranged for a helicopter to lower another salvage pump down onto our deck, but the helicopter cannot take off or fly in the fog and other ships are offering to help us out with salvage pumps, but they can't see us. The water in the hold is gradually rising and the salvage pump is going flat out. We are losing the battle, and cannot see the full extent of the damage behind the bulkhead.

The old man tells the coastguard the only thing we can do now is to make a dash to the nearest port, and the coastguard orders us to turn around and head for Wick, which is 20 miles back. The old man does not waste any time and immediately puts the Corsair full ahead through the fog regardless, heading for Wick. The coastguard sends out a message to all ships to keep clear of the area!

You and Steve are on the bridge with the old man and Dale goes down to set a scenario plan ready to abandon ship. The Arctic Corsair is in a race for her survival and maybe our survival too, and her powerful Mirrlees engines are going flat out, but the faster she goes the more water is being pressured in through the damaged bow. The old man is an all-or-nothing man, and he is a very positive thinker.

Dale comes back onto the bridge after organising with the crew and tells the old man what he has arranged. If we have to abandon, the old man says it is a touch-and-go situation and, if the worst comes to the worst, he will stop the Corsair and get everyone safely into the life rafts and he will stay on board alone. He says he will ring her on full, try to make it to Wick and beach her to try to save her. Dale says, "No you won't. You will take to the rafts with us and let her go. There's no point in losing your life, Skip." But, as usual, the old man said nothing.

The Arctic Corsair is going flat out heading for Wick harbour in thick fog and we can't see a hand before us. We have to rely on the radar and the ship's siren and bell. All ships have been alerted to stay away from the area. The windows are open and the cold wind is swirling around the bridge and we don't know what is ahead of us and we are living on hope. The salvage pump is pumping water out of the hold onto the deck, and the lads are preparing an empty oil drum to use as a bailout on the end of the Gilson wire from the winch to scoop half a ton of water from the hold onto the deck, where it will run away.

Everyone is working above their expectations. The cook and Ralph bring us tea and sandwiches to the bridge. The cook is an exceptional man. You respect him for his helpful gesture in this situation. Ralph is very nervous and he looks pale and drawn. He says his seasickness has gone because of fright. He asks if we will be okay and will we make it to the shore? We tell him yes, we will make it. Don't worry, just follow what you have been told and stay by the cook's side. The cook says, "I will take care of him, and the deckie learner too." The cook is a brave and reliable man.

We are going full speed in a race to the shore and we have 10 more miles to go to Wick. The salvage pump is pumping the water out of the hold and the lads have got the winch going and they are bailing the water out using an oil drum with the lid cut off through the hatch and onto the deck. We can normally judge the trim of the ship by matching the bow against the horizon to tell us how deep the bow is in the water, but not in this case, because we can't see the horizon though the fog and it's obvious that the bow is going down deeper in the water. We are 8 miles from Wick and all the shipping in the area have been told our position and that we are steaming full in the fog and we may have to abandon. You and Steve are taking turns at the wheel and sounding the siren every two minutes and ringing the bell. The old man is trying to decide if to abandon the Arctic Corsair – it would be for the safety of the crew, because she could sink fast within minutes and take everyone down with her – or take a chance and carry on to Wick.

There is 8 miles to go to Wick, which will take half an hour, and we are trying to assess how deep we are in the water and if the hold is filling up fast. The question is: can we last for half an hour?

The sparks has passed our situation on to the coastguard, who came back and ordered us to beach her at Sinclair's Bay, which is 3 miles closer than Wick, saving fifteen or so minutes. The old man settled for that straight away, and sent Dale down to organise a scenario practice for the beaching and the impact, but still stand by to abandon the abandon because we don't know which one is going to happen.

Dale tells the crew to find a safe spot away from flying objects with our backs to the wall and sit down with our life jackets on for protection. The Arctic Corsair weighs the same as 700 cars and will hit the beach at 16 mph, so be prepared. We have fifteen minutes before impact or, perhaps, to abandon.

The lads are getting organised and the nervous channels are at the limit just waiting for the unknown to happen. The cook has the two lads with him sat down with their backs against a solid wall, and the crew have all found a safe place for the impact and are ready for what is to come. The old man and Dale and you and Steve are staying on the bridge and the sparks has found a safe place in the radio room to be near the radio.

The plan is finalised and the old man tells the lads who are bailing out on the deck with the oil drum they have done their jobs and to go find a safe place for the impact. The coastguard comes over the airwaves and says the emergency services have been alerted at Sinclair's Bay, and are waiting on standby. Our location has yet to be identified and they are tracking us on the radar. All we can do now is to wait.

The old man says the worst thing about our situation now is that we can't choose a spot to beach and we can't avoid any obstacles in front of us because we can't see anything. We are blindfolded and have no option but to take a chance and hope for the best. The time has come and we are racing to run the Arctic Corsair onto the beach. It's not known if it's sandy or rocky, and the old man, Dale and you and Steve are braced with your backs to the front of the bridge. The sparks is in the radio room and the crew and engineers are in the accommodation. The chief engineer is staying down in the engine room so he can see to the engines immediately after impact.

The last few seconds are the worst. The lads are all prepared and in their positions and the seconds feel like a long time, then the impact comes and it seems to blank your mind out. Nearly 700 tons of steel hits the beach at 16 knots and the brakes are hard, and there's the sound of banging, grinding and holding on. Then the momentum begins to ease and she comes to a stop, laid over at ten degrees on her port side.

We just sat there waiting for our wits and energy to come back. The chief engineer stopped the engines immediately after impact and everything went quiet except for the engines idling and the generators whining.

The old man is the first to move and says, "Let's see where we are, and see what the beach is like." We all find the energy to stand up. Dale tells you and Steve to go down and see if there is anyone needing medical assistance and what the situation is down there and come back to the bridge, telling the sparks so he can report it to the emergency services. He tells the crew to prepare to assemble all together, ready for when the emergency services arrive.

You and Steve go down to the accommodation where the crew are trying to get over the grounding. One man has a shoulder injury because he did not get braced for the impact properly and he was thrown, but the cook and the two lads are safe. We tell the crew to leave their bags and everything behind in the messdeck and they will be picked up and taken to the hotel later. All hands have to muster on the foredeck as they are and wait for the emergency services to take us off. The crew are badly shaken and the fog is still thick. It's 7 p.m. and we can't see a thing in front of us. The emergency services are on hand, but they can't see us and ask us to ring the ship's bell. The spark says they can hear us and are on their way. The lads are shouting to them and they are answering us. The lads start to scramble over the rail on the port side onto the beach as the emergency services arrive.

Dale tells them to come back and stay on board. The rescue services tell us to gather together so they can make a head count, to make sure no one is missing. It is low tide and the Arctic Corsair is halfway on the beach with her stern still in the water. You can smell seaweed and the beach.

The rescuers ask if anyone who is injured needs a stretcher, and someone shouts, "How many stretchers have you got, because we all need one," to everyone's amusement.

It is dark and cold. There is a klaxon horn blasting out from the shore to guide us in and a guide rope for us to hold on to keep us in line together, and the emergency vehicles have got their headlights shining. The rescuers begin to lead us up the beach to safety. You take a look back at the Arctic Corsair and she is barely visible as we leave her behind and she seems to be watching us.

The rescuers lead us on to where the emergency vehicles are waiting. They take the man with a shoulder injury for treatment and have another head count to make sure no one is missing.

A coach pulls up to take us to a hotel. The media have turned up and are taking pictures and asking questions as we board the coach. The coach pulls away and drives slowly through the fog and the darkness; we cannot see anything. The driver must be driving on instinct, and we drive very slowly for quite a while until we pull up outside the hotel. People come out to greet us and the media are there again. The hotel staff lead us into the foyer, then to the dining room, where they tell us we can order what refreshments we prefer, and the phone is free for us to call home. The hotel is nice and the staff are polite and cannot do enough for us. Some of the lads ordered tea and coffee and some ordered beer, but coffee was mostly preferred because everyone was stressed and tired. The manager says they will show us to our rooms when we are ready and tells us there is room service if we need anything. We are shown to our rooms and they are top-class, with a TV and everything we need. You and Steve share a room and the lads are all sorted. There is an internal phone on which you can speak to people in other rooms.

The waiters tell us to go down to the dining room to order a meal after being shown our rooms. The cook, Ralph and the deckie learner go to the dining room. Ralph does not understand the situation and is uneasy, saying, "I don't have any money to pay for a meal." The cook tells him to go ahead and order what he wants because it's paid for. We order sarcly because we do not have much appetite and are tired, but we enjoy our meal and soon retire to our rooms.

We order beer in the room and some of the lads come to join us. We are all over-tired but do not want to turn in and spoil the magic of being safe in a posh hotel, so we go over what happened.

Dale and the old man come into the room, and the old man says he can't get over the collision and how we have lost the Arctic Corsair, but it was an accident that could not be avoided, and he will put it in the Board of Trade statement. Dale says we were minutes from sinking when we ran the Corsair ashore and if we had not made the dash when we did, things could have turned out a lot worse.

Some of the crew and the cook and Ralph pop in because they are not ready to go to bed yet, and they have all been on the phone talking to their families. Ralph said it's the first time he has been on a ship and everything is new to him and he was terrified when the cook told me to put a life jacket on and follow him to the life rafts and stay by his side.

He says, "I didn't know what a life jacket was, or how to put it on, and I didn't know what a life raft was. I did not know what to do or where to go, but we just followed what the cook told us to do."

The deckie learner agrees with Ralph and tells us how the cook had led him and Ralph through the terrible situation. The deckie learner is only 16 and comes from a tough Hessle Road fishing family. He has been brought up in fishing. He has done four trips to sea and is much more composed than Ralph, because the stories he heard from his family from being young have put him in good stead for these situations.

Ralph refuses a beer. He does not drink or smoke and he speaks with a slightly posh accent. He says, "If the food is free, I will eat as much as I can while I can before I go back on the streets. I have been homeless for three years, and I lived in a cardboard box behind a row of shops in Piccadilly Square in Manchester. I had to live by eating the outdated food from the skips and visits to the soup kitchens.

"They give me a bed for the night if there is one, and turn me back onto the street if there isn't one and I was an outcast and I lost hope. People look down on me and it is impossible to get a job because no one wants you, and I thought being a fisherman is my opportunity to have a normal life.

"But the bad weather and seasickness and the collision and the beaching has scared the life out of me, and I don't know what to do. I have nowhere to go from here. But I never want to go back on the streets again and I dare not go back on board a ship ever again because even the thought of it terrifies me."

Ralph says that he got some charity clothes given, and he had a shave and a shower at a hostel and hitch-hiked down the M62 to St Andrew's Dock in Hull. "I saw the Arctic Corsair coming home through the lock gates and thought what a beautiful sight it is, and someone showed me where the dock office was, and I spoke to the ship's runner. He had a look of understanding and kindness and told me to come and see him at 10 a.m. I was excited and I went to see if I could find some food. There are takeaways and fish and chip shops on Hessle Road, but I didn't have any money and I watched people throw their leftovers in the bins and took it out and ate it. I looked around for somewhere to sleep and found an abandoned car."

Ralph says he went to see the ship's runner the next morning full of nerves and he had the log book open and a pen in his hand and said, "Sign here and you are sailing on the Arctic Corsair at 6 a.m. on Thursday as galley boy, and do not be late." Ralph adds, "My knees were knocking and my hands were shaking and I was lost for words. I could not thank him enough, and on Thursday morning I was on board the Arctic Corsair and the watchman gave me a mug of tea and a sandwich and I sat waiting in the warm galley not knowing what was lying ahead of me."

Everyone needs sleep and we all go to our beds, but we do not sleep well and keep waking up to the reality of what has happened. Steve keeps getting up and sitting on his bed. At 7 a.m. a bell rings to tell us it is breakfast time. We have a shower and a shave with some disposable razors and go down to the dining room with the smell of coffee in the background. We order fresh orange juice and cereals and a fried English breakfast. Ralph orders breakfast and toast and is eating slowly with proper table manners. But it occurs to us that if anyone leaves anything, he will make a doggy bag of it to take with him. Steve speaks to the waiter when they are on their own and tells him Ralph's story, and if there is any food left after breakfast, Ralph would appreciate it in a doggy bag. The waiter tells Steve, "Yes of course. No problem!"

They call us out at 5 a.m. for early breakfast and our agent tells us we are setting out early to meet the flight schedule, and our sea bags are on the coach that will take us to Aberdeen Airport.

He says, "You have a flight booked for 12 a.m. on the Aberdeen Airbus that will land at Hull airport at 1.20. The coach ride to Aberdeen Airport takes three and a half hours."

The lads start making phone calls to tell their families what time they will be home. The fog has cleared and the coach is waiting outside the hotel to take us through the most beautiful Scottish scenery you can imagine to get to Aberdeen Airport. We have collected our bags and are starting to make our way to check-in. Ralph says he wants to say goodbye to us all, and he is going to stay here on the streets of Aberdeen because he has nowhere else to go. He stood there as he was, with no money and just a doggy bag of food in his hand. That is all he had in the world.

The old man is a hard and stormy ba****d of a fisherman, but he put his arm around Ralph's shoulders and we all looked on as he said, "Come with me, son," and he walked with Ralph to the check-in.

We check in and board the flight to Hull and Humberside airport. The cook sat with Ralph on the plane to give him confidence and, after take-off, the stewardesses dish the drinks out. "Doubles on the house, but only one, and after that, you have to pay for it."

The Aberdeen Airbus is a prop job and takes all the turbulence, but they are fine, and in an hour and twenty minutes we are fastening our seatbelts ready for landing.

As we come through the terminal, the ship's runner is waiting for us and begins to show his concern about what had happened to us and the Arctic Corsair. We collect our bags and board the coach laid on for us, and we set off for Hull.

Dale tells the ship's runner the story about Ralph having no money and nowhere to stay and that he will have to live on the streets. The ship's runner says, "I will arrange for Ralph to stay in the Fishermen's Mission with full board until he goes back to sea. I will make sure of that. We will drop him off there, and I will arrange it with them." Ralph looked scared at what was being explained, and he said nothing.

# Chapter 3
# Fight outside Rayners

The crew of the Arctic Corsair have arrived back home in Hull after surviving a collision with a collier in thick fog and leaving the Arctic Corsair on the beach at Sinclair's Bay. The news of the grounding has spread quickly around the streets of Hull and it is mentioned in the headlines of the *Hull Daily Mail*. Hull is no stranger to disaster, and the community always rally around to help each other when they are needed.

You have slept the clock around and wake the next morning feeling refreshed. You ring Steve and Dale and arrange to meet up in Rayners bar and go over what happened to the Arctic Corsair over a pint or two. The pub is packed and everyone knows each other and they are talking mainly about the things that have happened while they have been away at sea.

Dale goes to the phone and rings the office for any news of the Arctic Corsair. She is halfway on the beach and the stern was still in the water at low tide when we left her, so when the tide comes in she will be at the mercy of the sea, and if a gale blows up she will be finished. Dale comes back off the phone and the office have told him that the weather at Sinclair's Bay is good, and the surveyors have assessed the damage to the bow, and they think there is a chance they can weld her up while she is out of the water and tow her to Wick bay, depending on the weather. Dale said the weather is still flat calm at Wick, so it could give them a chance to weld and patch her up and make her seaworthy. The Arctic Corsair was specially built with a riveted rather than a welded hull, to give it extra strength to cope with the worst of the Arctic weather, and for ramming through the pack ice. We will know if they can refloat her when Dale rings the office tomorrow.

The ship's runner told Dale over the phone that the Arctic Buccaneer is coming off survey in ten days' time, and he has pencilled our crew in the log book for those of us who are ready to sail. You and Steve and Dale agree on that, and the rest of the crew will probably agree to it too.

We get the beer in and talk about the fog and collision, and the inquest we will have to face because we were on watch on the bridge when the collision happened. We finish our beer and walk down Hessle Road to the Halfway pub to meet the rest of our crew. There are a lot of characters drinking in there. The landlord used to play rugby for Hull and he and the landlady are very popular with the customers, going out of their way to help anyone. Dale tells the rest of our crew what the office have told him about signing on the Arctic Buccaneer in ten days' time, and they all agree to have ten days ashore and sign on the Buccaneer. We will have to sign on the dole tomorrow until she is ready.

One of the lads says, "Has anyone seen Ralph? I'm sorting my clothes out at home and I have got a three-day millionaire suit, and some other gear that will fit him if he wants it." One of the lads says they only live in Eton Street, around the corner from the Fishermen's Mission, so they will pop in on their way home to see if he is there, or if he's moved on.

The ships are coming home and the fish market prices are sky high and they are getting higher. Hull trawlers are breaking world records for money and tonnage again and again, and St Andrew's Dock is an outstanding workhorse for the country. The Hull trawler owners are elite businessmen, and they balance their rotas to bring the trawlers home to land their fish and get them back out to sea to meet the ever-increasing demand for prime white fish: cod, haddock and halibut. The fishing industry is Hull City Council's greatest asset to its economy, which is said to be one of the richest in the country.

It's 17 October 1967, three days after the Arctic Corsair collision. It's 8 a.m. and the old man's wife rings Dale and tells him that the old man is depressed about the collision and is not sleeping. He is not himself and keeps telling her he has lost the Arctic Corsair. Dale tells her we can all meet in town because none of us feels good about it and an afternoon out will help us all. Dale tells her that he will arrange for you and Steve and the wives to meet around eleven o'clock in the Punch Hotel in Victoria Square, where the old man usually drinks. Steve picks you and your wife up in a taxi and we go into town. Dale and the old man and their wives are already in the pub waiting for us. The women are great pals and are happy to meet up and chat among themselves while we catch up on the latest news of the Arctic Corsair over a few drinks.

The old man soon becomes his old self again when someone asks, "Where shall we go for a meal?" The old man suggests Carver's fish and chip restaurant. His wife pipes up and says, "No, we will not. We are going for a proper meal." The old man laughs, "So there is someone in the world who can tell the old man what to do."

We have another round of drinks and decide on going to Hammonds restaurant just a short walk from where we are now, and we can have a drink with our meal too.

We set off to walk across to Hammonds when, to our surprise, Ralph comes walking toward us, shouting, "Hello. It's me. It's Ralph," and he is very happy to see us.

We're all very pleased to see Ralph and we introduce him to the ladies. He is dressed very smartly in a three-day millionaire suit, shirt and tie. The lads have smartened him up, his hair has been cut short, and he's had a shave and looks like a typical Hull fisherman. The wives are asking who he is and we tell them he is the galley boy. The ladies tell Ralph they are very pleased to meet him. Ralph tells us he popped his head round Halfway's door, and the crew were in there drinking and they bought him a shandy because he doesn't drink.

"They took me to one of their houses where they were having a party and they dressed me up in this three-day millionaire suit, and they said how well I look and how well I play the part as a fisherman. They gave me money to get my hair cut and people were nodding to me as I walked along the street to the barber's, and it made me feel special. The barber asked me what ship I'm in."

The old man is as tough as they come but he has a caring side to him, and he said to Ralph, "Come and join us, Ralph. We are going to Hammonds restaurant for a meal, and I'm paying. So come on."

We are settled in Hammond's and the staff set the tables up to make one big table. We order our meals and Ralph orders a mixed grill and the old man orders fish and chips, which is followed by some amusing comments from his missus, like how he lives on fish! She says, "He will have it for breakfast, dinner, and tea if I put it in front of him."

The ladies laugh and grow fascinated with Ralph, who tells them about living in Piccadilly Square behind the shops in a cardboard box for three years, and living on out-of-date food from skips. Or he would watch someone eating a takeaway in the street and wait until they put it in the bin and he would take it out and eat what was left, and how the tramps fought over cardboard boxes to sleep in. He says he lived in constant fear of being murdered. If he found a box and there were not enough boxes to go around, the tramps would drag you out.

"They would tip your box over, and tip you out, and kick you and rob you and you are left with nowhere to sleep, and it happened every night and I lived in constant fear. I was a down-and-out outcast and no one would help me to get back into society. So when I heard about Hull's fishing trawlers I thought, *If I can hitch a lift to Hull, and get a job on a fishing boat I will have a bed and food and money to live on, if they will have me.* I had become down and out and I lost confidence in myself."

It is a fascinating story and Ralph goes on to say in word-for-word detail: "I did get a job on a trawler and I went to sea on the on the Arctic Corsair, and I never have felt so poorly in my life being seasick. We were in a force-eight gale as soon as we got out to sea. I have never been so scared when the next day in fine weather we collided with another ship in thick fog and we had to put life jackets on and stand by the life rafts ready to abandon the ship and the water was coming into the hold and the ship was sinking, and the ships sired and bell was sounding every two minutes and Dale told the crew and the engineers to get the salvage pump ready. Then he told us that we were sinking because the salvage pump could not cope with the amount of water that we were taking in and the helicopters couldn't see to fly in the fog. It was scary when the old man made a touch-and-go decision to go full ahead for 20 miles to Wick and try to run the Arctic Corsair ashore.

"Then Dale told us to prepare for the beaching impact and still keep the abandon-ship scenario in place. He told us to find a place to brace ourselves for the impact that will follow, which were the longest few seconds of my life."

Ralph said it was much scarier than spending a night behind the shops in Piccadilly and the threat of being murdered by tramps. "And I'm still shaking with fright because I did not understand the situation that we were in, and it's like being afraid of the unknown."

The ladies asked Ralph if he was going back to sea after his ordeal. He said, "I have a choice of going back to sea even though it's dangerous being a fisherman, or going back on the streets, which is an existence to nothing and being a nobody, and I think I might go fishing again because the people in Hull have given me new hope. They smile and speak to me and I wear a fisherman's suit like I belong here and this is where I want to be. I live in the safety of the Fishermen's Mission with a nice bed and nice food and plenty of friendly people to talk to and I am grateful."

Dale asks Ralph if he has been down to see the ship's runner about joining the Arctic Buccaneer in a week or so, and Ralph says he goes to see to the ship's runner regularly and his name is pencilled in on the Arctic Buccaneer's log book.

The ladies wish good luck to Ralph. They tell him the old man and the crew will take care of him. They have enjoyed his company and are looking forward to seeing him again after the next trip.

We walk through the town centre and it is teeming with shoppers. The big-name stars are lit up performing in the nightclubs and ballrooms. Hull is thriving and a nice place to live. There are hot dog stands and fish and chip shops on every street corner and every pub is full of happy people. At St Andrew's dockland you can watch the trawlers coming in and sailing out on the tide and there are scores of taxis bringing the three-day millionaire fishermen down to the pay office to collect their money and taking them back into town to spend it on anyone and everyone that wants to join their company. Visitors from other towns and cities are amazed at the activity in Hull.

It's 20 October 1967 and the office tell us the Arctic Buccaneer will be ready to sail on the 24th after she comes off her survey, and most of the Arctic Corsair's crew are pencilled in to sail on her. The latest news on the Arctic Corsair is that she has been welded up and refloated, and she is in the safety of Wick harbour and on schedule to be towed back to Hull on the 22 October fine-weather window. She will go into the dry dock to have a complete survey. The surveyors say she doesn't look any worse for wear after the beaching, but it's early days and they don't know yet.

It's Monday 23 October 1967 and the Arctic Corsair's crew have been ordered down to the office to sign on the Arctic Buccaneer's log book. You and Steve arrive in a taxi and the lads are standing outside the office after they signed on. The lads tell us we are sailing on Wednesday 25 at 9 a.m. You ask the taxi driver to wait for you. The ship's runner gives you your orders and tells you not to be late, and he gives us a note for the stores.

Some of the lads are going into Stanton's Cafe for coffee and hot cakes before they go off the dock, and we arrange to meet later. We have today and all day tomorrow ashore, and time to pack our bags and get a case of beer and a bottle of rum or whisky to take away with us.

Steve says he didn't see Ralph or the cook. I wonder if they have signed on or not. The taxi takes us to Rayners bar and it is packed out. There are plenty of staff serving; you are never kept waiting, no matter how full the pub is. The pub is on Hessle Road, on the corner of West Dock Avenue, just a ten-minute walk from the dock, so it is a handy pub to get to.

The domino players are rattling their dominoes and having friendly arguments, and someone shouts. There's a fight outside a school yard and everyone stops what they are doing and goes to the windows to see what is happening. The bar staff stop serving to watch the fight. It is between the two local scrappers who would take anybody on. They loved to fight just for the sake of it. They fight for a long time and Ginger the policeman stands there watching (he never interfered in a fair fight). He says it is best to let them fight it out because they will still fight it out later anyway even if he stops it. They fight to a standstill and are both worse for wear, and they come back in the pub bleeding and gasping for breath, but they refuse to shake hands because they say it isn't finished yet – there's more to come and they will finish it tomorrow. They most certainly will, and after it finishes, everyone goes back to what they were doing as if nothing has happened, and the bar staff start to serve again as normal.

It's 25 October 1967 and most of the crew of the Arctic Corsair have signed on the Arctic Buccaneer after her survey and refit. You are ready to sail again. Your dreaded routine of leaving home to go to sea is here again. Your nervous channels have started and you are waiting for the taxi to take you down the dock. You feel sick and your family are unhappy and saying their farewells and the dog is looking sad. The taxi arrives and you pick up your bags and put on a brave face and go out to the taxi where Steve and the lads are waiting. The curtains start twitching and neighbours in the street stop talking and they watch you get in the taxi. The kids stop playing in the street to watch the taxi drive off. You look back and wave from the rear window. The feeling is hurtful, but every fisherman gets the nerve channels when they go away. We drive through the railway tunnel and onto the dock and pull up just past at the Lord Line building where the Arctic Buccaneer is tied up. We get out of the taxi and climb aboard her with our bags.

But on this ship the crew sleep all together in a twelve-man fo'c'sle forward in the bow. You choose a suitable bunk and throw our bags in it. You don't need to go to the stores for anything this trip. The lads are having a can and a dram. It's the only comfort we have apart from each other's company, and it helps to have drink when you're going away. All the crew from the Arctic Corsair are here except for three new crew members, and the sparks is here too.

The ship's runner greets us and wishes us well, but he is always eager to get the ships away as soon as everyone is on board and he is shouting, "Everyone ashore who are going ashore. Stand by to let go."

The telegraph rings to stand by, and the engines begin to rev up, and the visitors scramble ashore, the crew go out on deck and pull the ropes in. The

Arctic Buccaneer goes astern from the moorings and stops, then she goes slowly ahead through Hull's sacred lock gates between the ladies of the Fisherman's Charter protest quay, on the port side, and the Bullnose quay on the starboard side. People are lined up on the quay shouting and waving their farewells, and shouting wisecracks like, "Bring 'em back alive" at the old man on the bridge, and that sort of thing (which is accepted), to the amusement of the onlooking crowd. The old man rings the Arctic Buccaneer full ahead. The screw churns up the water and we surge ahead. The old man blasts a cock-a-doodle-do on the ship's siren, and the streets of Hessle Road know the ships are sailing. You take a look back and feel sad and the only way to get over it is to have a dram or two with the lads.

Dale comes into the fo'c'sle to set the watches, and you and Steve are on watch with him from dinner to tea. He tells us the Arctic Corsair has been welded up and she is on her way back to Hull escorted by two tugs. The Met office have predicted a weather window with fine weather for the journey from Wick to Hull. We will pass her on the way but it's doubtful we will see her because they will probably hug the coastline, but maybe not if the weather's fine.

The anchor chain is banging and the lads are sorting a bag becket out and pass it up the anchor flu to take the impact of the chain to stop the noise.

Someone puts a shovel of coal in the stove that is our only source of heating. The lads are putting curtains made from their blankets across their bunks to keep the light out because the lights have to be kept on all the time because of the activity of twelve men. They are all packed into one berth. There is no privacy at all in a fo'c'sle. We get snoring, bad habits, things rolling about in a locker, and people whispering so as not to wake you up, or a smoke blowback from the stove when the wind gets in the wrong direction. You get woken by someone cussing and swearing when something has gone wrong and someone else shouting to tell them to shut up.

We pass Grimsby tower to starboard and go round the Spurn lightship anchored 5 miles to the seaward. Spurn lightship is painted red and she can't be mistaken. The watch are called to the bridge and we are out of the River Humber and in the North Sea. You, Steve and Dale take the first watch. The old man sets a course for Iceland, and the Arctic Buccaneer is going full speed ahead.

You soon get used to sailing on a different trawlers, because everything is basically the same but with a different layout. We sleep forward, and we have to run across the deck and risk our lives when we change watches. We have to leave the bridge and climb down the casing onto the deck to get to the galley and the after accommodation where the cook and galley boy and the engineers and bosun sleep. There have been a lot of people lost overboard when changing watches or trying to get to the messdeck at watch times and meal times from the fo'c'sle. Galley boys are not allowed on the deck at all, and if any of the crew goes on the deck, he is watched all the time, but if he is swept overboard by a wave, there is nothing anyone can do to save him.

The Arctic Buccaneer is going flat out heading for Iceland and the weather is fine with just a northerly breeze on our starboard bow. Steve is at the wheel and you go to the galley to make coffee and to see how things are. All the lads are for'ard in their bunks and there is pan of shackles left out on the stove, and bread and cheese and a few things left out on the messdeck table. It's 1 p.m.

The lads say Ralph is on board but we haven't seen him and you are wondering if he is seasick. You pop your head in the cabin where he sleeps and he is in his bunk with the light out.

You go round jamming things up that are rolling about. You make three mugs of tea and it is difficult to get back on the bridge carrying three mugs of tea because there are ladders to climb. The old man won't allow a kettle on the bridge because the steam can damage the radar and electronics, and it is the same in most of the ships, but we get by.

The engineer is in the galley starting the oil stove. He is getting it ready for when the cook turns out to get the tea ready. You notice a bucket of peeled potatoes jammed up in the corner that Ralph has prepared for tea, and you make your way back to the bridge with the tea. The remainder of the watch is uneventful and peaceful, and everyone except the watch and the engineers are resting in their bunks until it comes to 6 p.m. and teatime. Steve makes a dash from the bridge across the foredeck to call the watch for tea, then a dash back to the bridge. We keep an eye out for the lads crossing the deck until they get aft to the safety of the messdeck.

# Chapter 4

We are heading towards Iceland on the Arctic Buccaneer and it's breakfast time. The watch have been sent down to call all hands for a routine field day to get the trawl ready before we get to the fishing grounds and we are making the most of the fine weather. The old man and the sparks are giving the bond out at the same time. The sparks told us that the Arctic Corsair is under tow on her 525-mile journey from Wick harbour to Hull's St Andrew's Dock. The sparks told the old man she is just north of Flamborough Head and making good headway. The old man took special interest in what the sparks said and began to ponder on it.

We unbatten the hatches and get the trawl on to the deck ready to be fixed, and some of the lads go down to the fish room to get it ready. We usually have a bit of fun, a can and a dram and a sing-song while we're working on field days, and it can be enjoyable at times.

Ralph pops his head round the galley door to see what we are doing, and although the weather is fine, the movement of the ship is upsetting him and making him feel groggy, but he is doing well and the fine weather has done us a big favour and we get the work done. We finish the field day before dinnertime and go to the fo'c'sle for a can and a dram.

The cook has done a wonderful three-course meal, as he always does, and nothing is ever too much for him. Ralph and the tough little deckie learner have total respect for him; he is always there for everyone.

The afternoon passes and at 6.30 p.m. you, Steve and Dale go to the bridge and take over the watch. You are at the wheel and Steve is on lookout on the port wing. The old man is walking round the Arctic Buccaneer and taking things in and getting to know his new surroundings. He speaks to Ralph and gives him encouragement and Ralph tells him he feels a lot better. The old man speaks to the deckie learner, who is filling the net needles with twine and making settings ready for when we get to the fishing grounds. The deckie learner comes from a big, tough, no-nonsense fishing family from Hessle Road. He is a tough little 16-year-old Yorky who is happy to have his fishing career ahead of him.

The old man comes back on to the bridge and goes into the radio room to talk to the sparks. The old man comes from the radio room and alters course to slightly to the west and says, "Let's go and say hello to the Arctic Corsair on her tow home to Hull. We are at Flamborough Head and she is on course to pass us at some stage. We can't just sail by and ignore her. I would never forgive myself after what has happened to her, and she might bring us some good luck."

Dale switches the radar on to the 40-mile radius and watches for the likely pings of the Arctic Corsair and the two tugs escorting her. Steve goes down to the galley and makes some tea and Ralph helps him to carry it back to the bridge, because he wants to see the Arctic Corsair pass. Dale says he is pinging something on the radar ahead of us bearing down on our position and the spark can hear the tugs talking over the VHF radio. He has made contact with the tug master and tells him that the regular skipper and crew of the Arctic Corsair are here on board the Arctic Buccaneer and we hope to sail in her again when she has had her survey. The tug master wishes us good luck and says everything is fine on the tow and they will be passing us shortly.

An hour later, Ralph comes back onto the bridge after he finishing washing the pots and the Arctic Corsair is approaching us fast. It's surprising how fast the tugs are towing her; they waste no time as they pass us by. The old man gives a courtesy hoot on the ship's siren and the two tugs sound back. The old man says the Arctic Corsair always seems to be watching you as she passes us by. Her sleek, black-painted silhouette, white bridge and high masts stand out on the horizon as the distance grows between us. The old man says it has given him great satisfaction to see the Arctic Corsair being towed home, and we alter our course back toward Iceland's fishing grounds.

Things are a lot different when we all have to sleep forward in the fo'c'sle. We have to run across the foredeck to put coal on the fire or to call the watch, and even in moderate weather it can still be dangerous, because you have to time your run. It is hard to run across a ship's deck when it is pitching up and down and rolling from side to side, and you can find yourself left in mid-air or on your knees, or running sideways in the wrong direction and you can't stop. Sometimes, when the weather is bad and we are steaming, you would go without your dinner rather than risk running across the foredeck, and sometimes you would stay in the messdeck rather than cross the foredeck to your bunk.

The sparks says the weather is moderate at Iceland. We have another day's steam and the daymen are fixing extra gear and nets in the hold to save us work before we start fishing. The crew have settled down on board the Arctic Buccaneer and the next day we're called out to shoot. The ships are talking over the air that the fish has set in and the old man is pacing up and down with his fishing jersey on.

We shoot away, and we are on a fish shop (as we call it). It happens when all ships know where the fish is being caught and thousands of seagulls are following the ships and squawking and fighting over food. More trawlers ae arriving by the hour when they hear about the fishing. The trawlers are catching 200 kits a day, which is a good living. The weather is fine with no frost and it is quite warm. It's dinner time and the watch has been called. You, Steve and Dale go second sitting, then it's your watch below until teatime.

The cook has prepared an excellent meal, and Ralph is carried away washing the pots and is singing a song called the Swiss maid. He yodelled, "Yo lo lo lo lo, yo lo lo lo lo, yo lo lo lo lo laydyeeee," in a pitch-perfect Welsh soprano singing voice. The song is perfect for him. He says it's the only song he knows. Steve says wait until we get home and the wives hear you sing, and he says he loves to sing this and carries on singing. "Yo lo lo laydyeeee."

We have been fishing for a week and the fish is still here, even though there are a lot of ships filling their holds. It is top quality cod and haddock. But, all of a sudden, the fish take off and we are catching nothing. This is where the trouble begins, with the old man starting to experiment, looking for fish with no luck.

Our fish is fresh in the holds. We have caught 1,500 kits. That's 100 tons, and the owners have called us home for the best market. We lash the trawl alongside, clear the decks and batten down the hatches. We set off, full steam ahead for home before a force-five wind, and Ralph yodels a goodbye and farewell gesture to Iceland. "Yo lo lo laydyeeee, yo lo lo lo lo laydyeeeeee," and the lads yodelled along with him.

We do a twenty-one-day trip to Iceland and the weather is fair most of the time and there is plenty of fish there too: 100 tons of prime cod. The market is good and we make a bumper trip for the amount of fish we landed. Everyone treats Ralph, because the trawler owners don't pay galley boys any settling money, and they are hardly paid at all. Galley boys rely on what they are given by the crew. The trawler owners pocket every penny, even though galley boys are signed on the log as fully-fledged members of the crew, under the Board of Trade rules. A spokesman for the owners said: "It is part of learning the trade for galley boys and deckie learners to work their way up to full pay."

Ralph can't believe how much money the crew have given him after he settled. He says he will save it rather than spend it like the three-day millionaires do.

There are lots of taxis waiting to take the fishermen off the dock to wherever they want to go. The Arctic Buccaneer's crew have arranged to meet in the big Regent pub for the afternoon. You, Steve and Dale and your wives find a table near the window. The cook and his wife come in and join you and some of the crew and their wives and the old man and his missus all sit around. Ralph comes in with a girl who works in the Fishermen's Mission where he is staying. He has asked her out for the afternoon and brought her out to meet the crew. Everyone is dressed to kill, with pockets full of money. Ralph is wearing a black barathea suit with a shawl collar and half-moon pockets, a Spanish waistband and slightly flared bottoms, black shoes, a white shirt and black tie the lads have given him. He introduces his girlfriend as Norma. She has the same personality as Ralph. The ladies are pleased to meet her and to meet Ralph again. The wives are all speaking at once. Norma says she is very impressed with the company, and she is all smiles. The ladies tell Norma that Ralph is a lovely man.

Ralph, his girlfriend and the ladies get carried away in their conversations and we cannot get a word in edgeways The men talk about the fish sales and the quality control condemning perfectly good fish and the tally switchers. The old man says the owners have told him to stay home after this trip because the Arctic Corsair will be ready to sail after the new year. He has told the ship's runner that he wants to keep his crew together and try to give them priority to sign back on the Arctic Corsair if he can. The ship's runner said yes, no problem. The old man tells the cook he wants him to stay with him because he likes the way he fries his fish. The old man's missus hears what he says even over the noise of everyone speaking together. The old man says Arctic Corsair is having a full survey and refit and she is having a new automatic steering system installed.

Ralph has had four pints of shandy, equal to two pints of beer, so he is over the drink-drive limit, but he doesn't realise he is drunk. There is a singer on the stage, and you tell the wives how well Ralph can sing the Swiss maid. Norma has heard him sing it before, and the wives coax him onto the stage.

Ralph's high-pitched soprano rings out without a mike or backing music: "One day, a long time ago, on a mountain in Switzerland. Yo lo lo lo lo. There lived a fair young maiden, lovely but lonely. Yo-oh-oh-oh. I'd rather think that she did find her love, Yo lo lo laydee, Yo lo lo laddy eeeeee!" Everyone shouts for more, but Ralph says it's the only song he knows.

It's 20 November 1967 and we are ready to sail again on the Arctic Buccaneer. When we come home, we will spend Christmas and new year at home and the crew will sign back on the Arctic Corsair. We are going to the White Sea this trip. The trawler owners want us to go there because of the market demand for the quality and type of fish from the area at this time of the year.

The old man has spent many years fishing around the North Cape of Norway and the Russian coast and Novaya Zemlya, and further east for the big flat fish. We sail out of St Andrew's sacred gates and down the River Humber to the Spurn lightship and enter the North Sea. We take a northerly course and pass Scotland and into the Atlantic and head for the White Sea fishing grounds. The trawler owners want fish, and money, and so do we. It has taken four and a half days to get to Novaya Zemlya and there is a bitterly cold wind chill. We have been fishing for two days and the deck is waist-deep in cod and haddock. We have been very lucky to find the fish and things could not be better. We are happy and singing and talking about making a good trip.

Then we hear rattle, rattle, clunk, and the old man has his head out of the window. He is looking through his binoculars and we can see a warship in the distance speeding toward us. Then we hear rattle, rattle, clunk and the old man closes the window again, when he feels the cold. Then rattle, rattle, clunk again and the old man is at the window again. A Russian submarine has surfaced about a mile away and is heading toward us, with a display of spray crashing over its bow.

Then boom, boom. The shockwaves hit us through the water. The warship is firing at us with blanks and we are worried the submarine might torpedo us. A helicopter appears and hovers above the mast and the downdraught is blowing us off our feet. A man is sat with his legs out of the door, pointing and waving for us to leave the area.

The old man is wondering how he can get out of this, because we are outside the fishing limits but are not doing anything wrong. We have found the fish and it's a good living, but there is no way out of this, because if the Russians say we are inside their limits we will have to leave. They could accuse us of spying and arrest us, and we could finish our lives working in a Siberian salt mine.

The old man shouts out the window to get the trawl on board. We have to leave. There are stories of military men taking jobs as radio operators on the Hull trawlers with special equipment on board, and many people are convinced that is true, but it has never been proven.

We get the trawl aboard and we are steaming full speed away from Novaya Zemlya, but the Russian navy are still observing us. We don't trust the Russians, because they are capable of sinking us and then denying it.

We steamed easterly for six hours to get well away from Novaya Zemlya. We start looking for a likely tow. The old man knows these waters and we try shooting here and there until we find the fish again. The old man experimented, and changed tows at our expense and tolerance, until we are up to our waist in good quality cod and haddock again.

It's 6 a.m. and it's breakfast time. We hear "Yo lo lo Laydyeee". It's Ralph yodelling along the deck to tell us that breakfast is ready. Ralph says he thought the Russians had hit us with a missile when the impact of the shockwave hit us. He said, "I was looking to the cook for assurance, but he was not sure if we had been hit or not. The watch below and the engineers got out of their bunks to see what had happened." Ralph says he did not even know we were in Russia, and that nothing surprises him any more.

It's 6 December 1967. The Russian navy had been harassing us at Novaya Zemlya, and we have moved to another fishing location out of their way. It's early morning and there is hardly a breath of wind, but it's very cold, and the sky is lit up with the aurora borealis or (the Northern Lights). They happen when a solar storm comes toward Earth. Some of the energy and small particles travel down the magnetic field lines to the North and South Poles. They are called the Southern Lights in the south and the Northern Lights in the north. They can even be seen from Aberdeen.

We have caught a cod with a tag on it and will take it home for the scientists to learn about the migration of fish and give them the location of where we caught it. We have caught a deformed cod which we will take home for research. We come across these fish everywhere we go, so we can't blame the Russian nuclear programme. They could have even travelled here with the Gulf Stream.

We have caught 1,800 kits of cod and haddock and flats, and the owners have called us home for the 12 December market. We stow the trawl and batten down the hatches and the old man rings the engines on full ahead for the four-day journey home. Ralph and the crew give out a farewell cry to Russia, yodelling "Yo lo lo laydyeeee". The sound is carried away with the wind. You, Steve and Dale are on watch from dinner to tea and we are glad the fishing is over. We can rest our sore wrists from the wear and tear of the last ten days.

We have been chased off the fishing ground at Novaya Zemlya by the Russian navy and finished our trip elsewhere. We are heading home with 1,800 kits of cod, haddocks and flats. The weather is moderate for this time of year and we are making good headway. The lads are playing canasta and crib in the messdeck with 60s music playing and Ralph and the cook are preparing the tea. The cook is the best around, with years of experience behind him, and he is teaching Ralph how to cook. Ralph is eager to learn and the cook stands back and lets him get on with it under his supervision.

The days pass and the lads get the ship spotlessly clean. The days are getting lighter as we go along, southerly. We are going for the early morning tide and pass Flamborough Head far off on the starboard side. Eventually we turn at Spurn lightship and into the River Humber. We pass the Grimsby tower on the way. The light on the Bullnose is green for go, and we go alongside the insurance buildings quay. We enter the sacred lock gates of St Andrew's. A tug tows us down the dock to our landing number place on the market. The old man rings the telegraph to finish with the engines and we get our bags ashore, heading for the waiting taxis and home.

It's the morning of 12 December 1967 and the Arctic Buccaneer is landing her fish from the White Sea. Hull's fish market is in full swing, with the clattering of clogs and the fish auctioneers shouting and men rolling kits of fish away and the barrow boys racing along with kits of fish on their barrows.

You and Steve are on the fish market and have come down for your fish to take home, and Dale is there giving out fish passes to the crew. He gives us a dram of whiskey. He tells us our fish is in big demand and it's looking good. The quality control has left us alone. There is a lot of hustle and bustle. The fish merchants and buyers and bobbers are all giants in their four-inch-high wooden clogs with studs in the soles so they don't slip. They have lots of clothes on to keep them warm that make them look even bigger, and their scary, loud voices are trained for shouting.

It's time to go back home for a bath and get ready for settling day. At 11 a.m. Steve and his wife pick us up in a taxi and we go down to the office. The ship's runner says, "If you want to wait for the Arctic Corsair, you will have to sign off the Arctic Buccaneer now. The Arctic Corsair won't be ready to sail till after the new year."

Steve signs off the Arctic Buccaneer and shoves the pen in your hand. We can have Christmas at home, but we'll have to go easy on our money. Most of the crew do the same, mainly to stay home for Christmas.

We go up to the settling office to get our money, then down to the waiting taxi that takes us into town for the afternoon. It's always very busy in the town, and we meet lots of fishermen with their wives all dressed to kill and loaded with money. We go into the Regent to meet up with the crew and their wives.

Dale and the old man are already seated there. Ralph is there telling the wives about the Russian navy shooting at us and submarines surfacing and a helicopter hovering above us with a man in the doorway looking down with a machine gun beside him, pointing at us to leave. He goes through the full episode word for word without missing anything. He tells them about the aurora borealis too.

Most of the crew are staying home for Christmas to go back in the Arctic Corsair, and the cook and Ralph are waiting at home for her too. Ralph is learning to cook and is very excited about it. His girlfriend, Norma, is telling the ladies how he made some coconut macaroons and hot cakes in her mam's oven. Later, we are going shopping to buy the stuff for tomorrow's dinner that Ralph is going to cook for her and her mam. He is going to cook the fish he brought home for tea tonight.

Ralph says he does not know whether to take home cod or haddock because he doesn't know which is best. The old man's ears prick up, but he doesn't say anything. The cook tells us that if you want to make a choice between cod and haddock, based on nutrition, cod is the winner because it has less cholesterol and sodium, but more polyunsaturated fatty acids than haddock. Plus, cod is thicker and meatier than haddock and has a bland taste, while haddock has a fishy taste, but haddock is a wonderful, healthy option, the same as cod.

The cook is a man of the world and he always amazes people with his knowledge, because he is never wrong. His biggest fan is Ralph.

After today, we have a few weeks to get over, skimping on our money by watching the TV and lazing around with Christmas and new year to look forward to before we sign back on the Arctic Corsair and head back to Iceland. We'll be doing that in the worst two weather months of the year: January and February.

# Chapter 5

It's 12 January 1968 and most of the crew have signed back on the Arctic Corsair, and we will be sailing on the 14th, in two days' time. We have had Christmas and new year at home and have been spoiled. We walk off the dock to Rayners Pub, just a ten-minute walk away, and it is packed as usual. We speak to some of the lads who have just got home from Iceland and they tell us the weather is really bad and the wind was blowing hard all the way home. They tell us we need to take our long johns and fearnots and mittens with us this trip because it's so cold.

We have a few pints and see our taxi driver in the pub. We order our cases of beer and bottles to take away with us and keep it in his boot until he picks us up on sailing day, and we have two days to get used to the idea of sailing again. January is one of the worst times of the year for weather, wherever you go in the northern hemisphere, and especially in Iceland. None of us are looking forward to it, but fishing is our job. That is what we do. The same old going-away routine begins.

It's 14 January and the taxi is wating at your door. You say goodbye to your family, who are all upset, and even the dog looks sad. You put on a brave smile and walk out to the taxi where Steve and some of the lads are waiting. There are curtains twitching and some of the neighbours are talking on their doorsteps and they give you a wave. The kids stop playing in the street and watch you get into the taxi. They shout to you "Have a nice trip" and they wave. You look back from the taxi's rear window as it drives away. You talk to your shipmates and settle down a bit, but they are all secretly feeling it.

The taxi pulls up at the Lord Line building where the Arctic Corsair is waiting and she is watching as we get out of the taxi. You climb on board her to the familiar sounds of the engines idling and her generators whining and the smell of diesel and raw vegetables and fresh paint in the air. We are greeted by the rest of the crew. The ship's runner is eager to get us away while we are all on board and he shouts everyone ashore who is going ashore and stands by to let go. The telegraph rings and we go stern and then stop, then slow ahead through the sacred gates. Then the old man rings her on full ahead, and the Arctic Corsair seems raring to go, and her screw churns the water up astern of us and the old man gives a cock-a-doodle-do blast on the ship's siren to tell the Hessle Roaders the ships are sailing. You take a last look back and watch the Bullnose and the sacred lock gates and the quays and there is a silent whisper in your mind saying, "You will be home soon, don't worry!"

After getting over us leaving home, it feels good to be back on board of the Arctic Corsair, and you get a strange feeling she is glad the crew are back together. We sail up the river and pass Grimsby tower and make a U-turn around the Spurn lightship and we are clear of the river and into the North Sea. You and Steve are on watch with Dale the mate. Dale is at the radar and Steve is at the wheel. You go to check around the ship to be sure everything is safe. The Corsair is rolling and you begin to get used to the roll as you make your way down to the accommodation. Some of the crew are in their bunks and some are having a dram or two, and holding on as they go. The cook and Ralph are in the galley preparing the tea. Ralph has found his sea legs after doing two trips in the Buccaneer and the cook said there is something loose on the boat deck and it is banging. You go up and sort the noise out and come back down to the galley.

Ralph asks if you like the gold cross Norma has bought him to keep him safe. Most fishermen wear a cross that their families have bought them. In Italian, it is called croce di oro (gold cross) and some fishermen call it a St Christopher (there is a song "So I give you this croce di oro to bring you home safely to me"). Ralph is very happy with his present from Norma, it means the world to him, and he says he will buy one for Norma when we get home.

You make three mugs of tea and take it to the bridge. You can hear the radio operator sending out a Morse message in the radio room. The Arctic Corsair has had a complete survey and she is in top condition. You can smell paint drying out and it gives you a headache.

The sparks comes to the bridge and tells us to look out for a man in a rowing boat in the vicinity. He left Bridlington to go sea fishing and has not been heard of for twenty-four hours. We will keep looking out for him, but it is unlikely we will find him in these weather conditions.

The Corsair's automatic steering problem is not fixed. We are still waiting for a spare part from Germany and it will be ready for the next trip. It's 6 p.m., teatime, and you call the next watch to relieve you. You have brought your tape recorder with you and stacks of tapes packed with 60s music. Ted the engineer has fixed a shelf in the messdeck for it. You have made a tape with the Swiss maid repeated on it for Ralph, but everyone likes the song too.

The next watch come on the bridge to relieve us, and Dale tells them we are looking out for the man from Bridlington in a rowing boat. We must still keep looking out for him. We go down to the messdeck. All the lads have gone to their bunks, and you, Steve, Ralph, the cook and Ted the engineer have your tea together. The cook tells us Ralph is a natural cook. He has made the tea all on

66

his own with the minimum of help, and it takes his mind off the poor weather we are in. You tell Ralph you have made a tape of the Swiss maid for him and he says he will play it as soon as Ted sets the recorder up. The first watch is always long and stressful after leaving home, and there is nothing else for you to do but to get in your bunk and drift in and out of sleep until dinner and watch time, and you always wake up feeling worse for wear.

We go to the bridge and receive the watch. The old man is looking out the window at the weather. We have left the North Sea and are in the Atlantic Ocean. We are leaving mainland Britain behind and there is a huge Atlantic swell coming from the west on our port side and a gale blowing up on our starboard bow. It is causing a confused sea, and the Arctic Corsair is going full ahead into it, and she is kicking up a heavy spray onto the bridge windows. As she goes over a wave and down into the trough, the bow scoops up the water with a jolt and throws tons of water into the air over the ship's structure. The power behind the impact depends on the speed of the ship meeting the power behind the wave. The ship is rolling and lurching heavily as she tries to cope with a confused sea and a head-puncher at the same time. You need both hands for yourself. The cook is not going to attempt to make a meal because it would be almost impossible, and it would be dangerous because the food and hot water would fly out of the pans, so he is making sandwiches. The Arctic Corsair is leaping out of the water and landing on its side one way or another, but the old man will not ease her in for anything. She has a powerful Mirrlees Monarch engine assisted by two turbines that are specially designed for speed, towing and reliability. She is built for the Arctic weather conditions and ramming her way through fields of pack ice, with a riveted rather than a welded hull specially made for strength. Her top speed is 16 knots, and you cannot hold her back; she is always raring to go.

The watches change day and night and this is not a nice place to be. We are getting thrown about and having to hold on. Everything that is loose is banging and crashing and you can't sleep. We are all in the messdeck after breakfast, and one of the lads says, "No matter where you go, there is always somebody with a bigger problem than yours." He adds that we are lucky, really, because we get free fish and chips. Someone shouts, "Why don't you shut up!"

There is no point in sitting in the messdeck in weather like this and it's always better to find a book to read and jam yourself up in your bunk and just keep out the way until it's your watch time, or if we run out of the bad weather. But, at this time of year, the weather is still usually bad even when it changes, and we just swap one piece of bad weather for another. But it is not always like that, because sometimes even in the winter you can get nice, fine weather, and it often happens.

We carry on crashing through the weather all the next day. And the next day. We are heading towards Iceland's fishing grounds. The old man is out and he has got his favourite fishing jersey on. He says, "We did well last trip so I told wife not to wash it, for good luck."

We can hear the ships talking over the air, and they are saying how bad the weather is and about getting their trawls aboard and going for shelter and safety. There is a gale blowing and all the ships are iced up. The Hull company Hendriksons have a fleet of older trawlers that take safety precautions seriously in bad weather, and they have not lost a ship in thirty years. That tells you a story, and their ships are taking cover under the lee of the land. The Grimsby trawlers are also sensible about safety to an extent, and they have all gone for shelter.

The old man is pacing up and down on the bridge in anguish, and if just one of the trawlers shoots his trawl, this old man will follow. Or it is more likely that this old man will shoot first anyway. The old man takes many chances against the weather, and he won't always get away with it. We have to trust him with our lives. There are twenty crewmen on a Hull trawler and twenty families to think about, but the old man will tell you we came out here to fish, we're not here on a holiday, and we have to take into account every day's fishing we lose.

The weather is worsening and all the trawlers are taking shelter or dodging up and down chopping ice, and the old man has no choice but to go under a lee until the weather goes away. All the ships are taking cover from the storm and we are chopping ice as we dodge it out. The old man tells Dale to call him if any of the ships start fishing and goes down to his berth. It's 2 p.m. and it's pitch-dark. The ship is steady but the wind is tearing through the rigging and we are iced up. Steve makes some tea and brings it up to the bridge. He tells us that the cook and Ralph are preparing the tea and making some bread. The weather is bad but the ship becomes steady when we are dodging.

The sparks is on the bridge and we talk about the weather and recall an unforgettable trip we did last April to Greenland last year. We were fishing very close to the land and the ice had broken up and was being taken round Cape Farewell with the currents and we were towing our trawl through the pack ice and catching lots of fish. It was daylight and, without any warning, a huge swell appeared from nowhere and the Arctic Corsair laid over and we didn't know what was happening. We shouted at the old man, "What is happening?" He replied, "I don't know." The swell came again and again through the pack ice field and we stopped gutting. We got out of the pounds, and the old man said he dare not attempt to get the trawl aboard because the swell was too big. The sparks was trying to raise the coastguard to report the incident and to find out what was happening. The coastguard said he would get back to us as soon as possible, but meanwhile we had to wait. The old man said we would carry on towing and we stood by with ice axes to chop the trawl warps away, rather than risk the safety of the ship. We had to know what was happening.

It was half an hour or so later that the coastguard came over the air with a tsunami warning and told us there had been a landslide that had caused a giant wave and advised us to wait it out until the sea state settled. The pack ice prevented it being much bigger. The old man asked if anyone had heard of a tsunami before, because it was new to him. It was new to us all.

The old man decided to haul and see if the trawl was still there, because the sheer weight of the amount of fish we were catching might have taken it away. We hauled on our beam ends, although the height of the swells was decreasing. The trawl had held but only just, because when we got the fish on board, the deck was full to the rail with tons of fish, which was rolling from side to side with the roll of the ship, and the old man brought her round into the swell to try to settle her down. We had to gut most of the fish and get it down to the fish room before we could think of shooting again, and the swell rapidly decreased back to normal. The coastguard said it was a landslide that caused it, but it could have been an ice fall from a glacier, we don't know.

Back to today, and we are sheltering from the storm under the lee of the land in Iceland and the old man has come on the bridge and is restless. He is pacing up and down on the bridge. The sparks goes into the radio room out of the way and all the conversation has dripped. The old man says he thinks the wind is decreasing. He seems to be waiting for someone to agree with him, but no one answers. He goes into the radio room and asks the sparks if any ships are dodging outside on the fishing grounds and the sparks says yes, but they are having a bad time of it. The old man says he thinks the wind is dropping, urging us to agree so we will go back out to the fishing location and dodge it out for a while. We leave the lee of the land and dodge back to the fishing grounds, but the wind has not dropped and the weather is terrible. It is too bad to fish in when we get there.

It's teatime and we change the watches, have our tea and get into our bunks, making the most of what we've got. We wait until they call us out to shoot. It's a scary time we are not looking forward to.

# Chapter 6

We're on the fishing grounds and it's early morning. The watch comes, banging on the berth doors shouting, "Down trawl, all hands, everybody out." They tell us it's blowing a gale and is 12 degrees below freezing, the seas are crashing aboard and we are badly iced up. It's a nightmare.

The lads are clamouring to get out of their bunks and get into their duck suits. The mood is grim and morale is low, and as we pass the galley we grab a mug of stewed tea that has been left on the cold stove since teatime and is awful. We have a smoke while the ship comes round into the shooting position. The ship is pitching and rolling with the heavy seas that are running. The telegraph rings to slow, and it's time go out on deck, when you realise how bad the weather really is. Your thoughts tell you that you should not be aboard here and your nervous channels are frantically sending out warning messages telling you to watch yourself as you try to get acclimatised to the wind, the sea spray, the cold, the darkness and the jerking movement of the ship.

The lads are complaining that the weather is too bad to shoot. The ship is rolling heavily because we have come round beam onto the heavy seas, and the floodlights are blaring in your eyes through the spray and darkness. The lads are tensed up as they take up their positions for shooting. We get the trawl outboard. And the noise begins, banging and bumping and chains clanging and men shouting. There is water splashing through the scuppers onto the deck and going out again when the ship rolls. It's wet and cold and you sense the images of your mates working beside you in their yellow duck suits. You can hear the sound of the bridge window go rattle, rattle, clunk when the old man opens it and quickly closes it again when he feels the cold.

There is only a metre-high rail and 18 inches of freeboard between you and the sea, and the deck is moving beneath your feet with water sloshing about when she rolls. It is hard to keep your balance, and every sound and movement tells you a message, and you know exactly what is going on as the trawl is paid away, and your conscience is reminding you that you should not be fishing in this weather.

We have fourteen days fishing ahead of us and we have started the trip off in these terrible, adverse weather conditions. Your energy drains quickly and we have to work fast for our own safety. We go through the routine of shooting in a desperate struggle until the afterman shouts "all square", which means the trawl is on the seabed and catching fish. We set the deck boards up and get the fish room ready to take the fish when it comes aboard. We have a quick drink and a smoke, and begin chopping the ice off the ship's structure. We are badly iced up, and we are starting to list to starboard. It's important to chop the ice off the structure, because water is heavy and can cause the ship to become unstable. Ice can quickly build up with wind spray that freezes instantly at minus 12. There can soon be a build-up of 20 tons of ice on the upper structure that could turn the ship over.

The fishing watches have been set, and the three-man watch go to their bunks for six hours. We have a breather and a drink and a smoke. We are dreading the task of hauling the nets in. Our nerves are on edge waiting. We have been towing along for two hours when the telegraph rings and it's time to go out onto the deck. The watch set the winch up and knock the towing block out. With a loud bang, the winch starts to haul the warps in. We all have our own position and our own job to do, and we work as a team. The ship turns beam-on to the wind and starts to ride over the sea swells.

The noises of banging, bumping and clanging of chains and the men shouting begins. Each man has his own job to do and we work together. We work at full speed to get the trawl inboard and the men watch out for each other at the same time. We finally get the fish inboard after some heart-stopping moments. Then we drop the nets back over the side, and shoot away again. The lads move quickly, and the winch begins to pay out the trawl warps until the trawl is all square on the seabed and catching fish. But we are unnerved, because we are fishing while other ships are sheltering and it's scary. You never know the minute, and anything could happen.

We sharpen our knives with the steel that is left handy in the washer rail in the fish pounds. We have caught sixty baskets of prime cod, what we call spraggs, and they are frozen stiff and still trying to wriggle. They are being frozen alive, because it is 12 degrees below freezing and the air we are breathing is as cold as the air in a fridge freezer. Fish will normally keep for nine days on ice at one degree before it begins to turn, depending on storage and air temperature. But in this case the fish is frozen alive. The fish room hatch is open and the frost at minus 12 goes straight down the fish room and the fish are actually being frozen alive at sea, so is fresher than fresh fish on ice.

We once asked the owners for some blocks of cardice to keep our fish fresh. The temperature of cardice is -7°C and it would help to keep the fish fresh in the summer, but the owners refused, saying it would be too expensive. But the real reason is that the trawler owners need to condemn some of our fish to keep their fishmeal and pet food factory supplied, so the cardice suggestion was rejected. Freezing the fish at sea, building bigger ships to catch more fish and keeping the ships fishing for months at a time was the secret plan we didn't know about at the time. The first of the Hull freezers – the Lord Nelson which was built in 1960 – is an example of things to come.

The cook shouts out for breakfast, just as we are finishing the fish and swilling down. We work faster to get off the deck. We have been working all night and are cold and hungry. The watch below have been called, we take our duck suits off and hang them in the drying room and go to the messdeck. There is porridge on the galley stove and a cooked breakfast of eggs, bacon sausage, beans and tomatoes and bubble and squeak, fried up from yesterday's left over veg, and a platter full of fried fish on the side. The cook makes all his own bread and hot cakes and pastry and a sweet for afters and he is looked up to as your mother (sometimes). They feed us well to keep the calories going into your diet. The owners know it will keep the men working, because an average man needs roughly between 2,000 and 3,000 calories or more each day, and the trawler owners make sure we get the calories and energy food we need to keep us working, and that we have enough fish, meat, potatoes and beans, etc. aboard.

The Icelandic weather is unpredictable and can change very quicky at times. As soon as breakfast is over, the ship starts getting thrown about. The telegraph rings and Dale the mate appears at the messdeck. He says the weather has sprung up unexpectedly and we've got hurricane-force winds and squalls and we will have to scramble the trawl aboard before we lose it. The lads start chittering and chafing, and swearing and cursing at the old man for being a lunatic.

We quickly make for the drying room to get our gear on, and Ralph is at the galley serving hatch wide-eyed. He is as white as a ghost and trying to grasp the situation. Dale tells the deckie learner to stay off the deck. The lads are having thoughts of their own in silence. They do not know what the others are feeling, or what is in their minds; no one speaks or says anything as they do their best to cope with the situation. We must follow our well-practised routine and rely on each other for safety.

We set the winch up and knock out the towing block and begin to haul the trawl up. The lads take up other own positions and wait for the trawl doors to come up. Dale shouts, "Play smart lads and watch yourselves."

The wind is howling and the sea is blown into white streaks of foam and the sea is being blown flat in the violent squall. The winch is struggling with the pitch and roll as it pulls the trawl warps in and the lads are tensed up and ready. Everything you do on a sidewinder trawler is done in the open, and we have to haul beam-on to the weather and keep the nets streamed out to stop them from going under the ship. There is no shelter for us at all. The trawl comes up alongside and the lads move in quickly, at the same time having to watch the sea and watch out for each other and do their job as best and as quickly as they can.

The bosun is old and slow and he is stood waiting to throw the chain into the after door, and he is exposed to the danger of the sea. The lads are watching him and shouting for him to get out of the way and "I will do it. I can get out the way quicker." But the bosun refuses, and his experience pays off again.

We drop the bobbins inboard and start to pull back on the bellies, standing on them to stop them from pulling back out. Then we hear the sound of a gigantic wave crashing towards us like an express train. The old man rattles and clunks the wheelhouse window down and shouts "Water. Look out. Get out of the way." Then rattle and clunk as he quickly closes the window again.

We have just seconds to get out of the way to safety. We climb up onto the casing and get behind the funnel or get wherever we can to get out of the way of the giant wave. It's an every-man-for-himself situation. The Arctic Corsair stands up for the challenge as she struggles to cope with the giant swell that has hit us beam-on. She lies over to port and her decks are flooded with water and she wallows and lies over to starboard again. The ship's rail vanishes under the wave and there is still tons of ice high up on the structure affecting her buoyancy. The weight of a 5-ton Granton trawl and of the catch all on the starboard side are adding greatly to the safety of the ship. The Arctic Corsair is lying further over, and then she steadies as though deciding which way to go before slowly coming back up, in control again. The deck is awash with water and the bellies have pulled back out as the ship tries to settle down.

The bosun shouts, "Is everybody here?" We have no time to waste and go back on deck, pulling back on the bellies, giving it everything we've got.

One of the lads has been knocked over in the scramble and filled his boots. He's soaked with freezing water and is breathing in sharply with cold-water shock. The man loses his temper and starts shouting and swearing at the ship as though it is the ship's fault. He is shouting "You mucky b*stard." He empties his boots, puts them back on and carries on working, even though he is wet and in pain with an injured neck and shoulder. Fishermen always stand by their mates and stay on the deck in difficult times, and the man carries on working.

The old man brings the Arctic Corsair slowly into the wind for safety. But there is still a danger that a sea can drop aboard and do a lot of damage.

We finally get the trawl lashed up along the ship's rail and the lads are greatly relieved. We take our gear off in the drying room and are exhausted. The cook has made a kettle of fresh tea for us, and we are more than ready for a drink and a smoke in the safety of the messdeck. The lads are chittering and complaining and talking about the scramble and the dodgy moments that we were lucky to get away with. Ralph is in the galley taking in every word. The old man shouts down the speaker for the watch to go on the bridge as we start to dodge through the storm to the lee of the land.

The man who got knocked over has a shoulder and neck injury and a man is suffering from a tooth infection. He has not eaten or slept for days and is in a poor state of health because he can't eat or drink.

The engine room needs spares, and we have no cooking oil. We are using cod liver oil for cooking and frying, from the cod liver oil boilers where we boil the fish livers. Some of the lads don't like it, but we did not know at the time that cod liver oil is high in vitamins A and D and it is full of the very vitamins we are lacking because of the lack of sunlight and natural light, because it is dark all the time in the winter. Vitamins A and D are known as the sunshine pills to take in winter.

The radio operator is sending out a report to Reykjavik that we have two men in need of medical assistance and need ship's stores and engine room spares. We receive an immediate reply and are given permission to proceed into Reykjavik and await further instructions. There is a truce in the cod war disputes that have been going on and off for years and there is still tension between the Icelandic and UK governments.

The old man sets out a course heading for Reykjavik. The wind is gusting at up to 60 mph on our starboard bow and we cannot avoid making ice, no matter how fast or slow we go. But the old man rings her on (as he does). It's 2 p.m. and it looks like we will be having sandwiches for tea, but the cook makes sure we get fed, whatever the weather.

The ice spray is gathering on the upper structure and on the bridge top, and everywhere. The temperature is minus 11 and we have got a four-hour steam to go yet. We might have to stop to chop ice for an hour or so because the ship is getting heavier, but the old man will keep going for as long as he can to get to Reykjavik and get back out fishing again.

You, Steve, Dale, the sparks and the old man are all stood in silence on the bridge looking out the windows in the dark, and no one is speaking a word. That is the mood we are in. It's five o'clock and we still have an hour to go before we get there. Dale suggests to the old man that we stop and chop ice because we are starting to list to starboard. We all wait for the old man to respond and he says, "We will be there under the lee of the land soon." Our nervous channels start to kick in and we are getting worried if we are going to make it.

We carry on in silence. The ship is rolling and getting heavier with ice. The shore lights are visible and we have not far to go. The mood begins to get happier. Steve goes down to check round to see if things are okay and the sparks went with him to help him back with the tea. The ship is getting steadier by the minute under the lee of the land and we can see the lights shining from the wooden houses in the village. We can see the wind blowing the snow off the land, creating a swirling mist.

We are under the lee of the land and the ship is much steadier, with a heavy list to starboard with the weight of the ice. The lads come onto the deck to get the mooring ropes ready and they are shocked to see the ice build-up that has gathered. They get the ice axes ready to start chopping it off.

We are welcomed by a British warship tied up at the quay. HMS Protector is an ice-breaker here on manoeuvres, and dozens of sailors are on the quay paying special interest in us. They take our ropes and put them round the bollards. They say, "It's nice to see you. How nice of you to visit." They are very friendly and amusing. They watched from the quay in amazement and commented on the ice build-up and a dangerous starboard list. They are fascinated as we start to chop the ice from the structure and from the bridge top with axes, and they watch as we shake the rigging with the Gilson from the winch to shake the ice off the top that we can't reach.

A taxi comes for the injured lads and takes them to hospital for treatment.

A navy officer called Johnny the one! is sent by the captain of the HMS Protector to invite the crew of the Arctic Corsair over for a courtesy visit when we have got the Arctic Corsair shipshape and safe. We are delighted at the invitation and it is a great change for us all. The sailors escort us from the Arctic Corsair along the quay to the warship. They are friendly and carefree and constantly making friendly jokes. They don't seem to care about anything and they stand guard on the quay to watch over the Arctic Corsair while we are their guests aboard the HMS Protector. The navy are concerned about the ice build-up and the list and our stability.

The sailors lead us to a messdeck where there were sandwiches and coffee laid out for us. To our surprise, there is a rum bosun dishing out rum and gin from barrels, in large crystal glasses, and they even bring in a rock group with guitars and drums to play for us. They play well.

The old man and Dale are led to the ward room to meet the top brass. The sailors make amusing jokes about everything and nothing escapes them. They joke when Ralph asks for a cup of tea because he doesn't drink. They even joke about the Arctic Corsair being iced up with a dangerous list to starboard. They joke about us having to chop the ice off the ship's structure. But, joking aside, they are very concerned about our situation and they tell us so.

But it doesn't take long before are making fun of things too, and enjoying it. The sailors say they would soon sort the old man out for us if he was here. Everyone is laughing, and when the old man and Dale came down to the messdeck, he starts to laugh with us too, but he doesn't know what we are laughing at, and the sailors say nothing to the old man out of respect for their own officers.

After an hour or two the two injured men return from the hospital and the sailors bring them into the messdeck for a drink and a sandwich. One man has a swollen jaw, and the other is wearing a collar around his neck. The injured men are more than amused at the jokes being cracked about them, and it is all good fun.

The old man says it is time for us to go, to make way for another ship coming in and clear the quay. The sailors give us one last dram and promise to carry us home if we can't walk. They escort us safely back along the quay to the Arctic Corsair, which stands proudly tied up alongside the quay. As usual, she seems to be watching as we climb aboard her. Her engine is idling, and her generators are whining, and she is ready to go.

The visit aboard the warship was an education, and we had a welcoming experience. The sailors line up on the quay and let go of our ropes and give us friendly waves and salutes. They tell us they have genuine concern for our safety and, as we pull away from the quay, they wish us good luck and good fishing. The sailors are true gents. HMS Protector has maybe 100 sailors or more on board. They are out on an exercise, training young recruits seamanship experience and to get their sea legs in bad weather, but it is doubtful they will be out in the full storm for long because they are packed like sardines in their hammocks and bunks and will get thrown all over the place. Your bunk is always the best and safest place to be in bad weather. HMS Protector will probably have a peaceful place to shelter when the weather gets as bad as this and there is no point in getting iced up. The Americans are giving protection to Iceland in return for locating their airbase in Keflavik, and the Americans are our best mates too.

# Chapter 7

You should never underestimate the Icelandic weather, because it can change at any time. The warm air from the Gulf Stream meets the cold air from the north and causes violent storms. The winter solstice begins on 23 December each year and, in 2015, the wind reached 160 km per hour, causing devastation. It came without warning from the met office. Without the heat from the Gulf Stream, the seas around Iceland and many other places would freeze over, including the North Sea, but in summer the weather can be pleasant, with long hours of daylight and sunshine.

We have been into Reykjavik to receive medical treatment for two of the lads and for stores and supplies. We have been under the lee of the land for the last twenty-four hours, sheltering from the storm. The wind is screeching through the rigging, wires and aerials, making terrifying sounds, and creating a piping sound in the background when the squalls get stronger and more severe.

The watch are on the bridge and the old man is showing his anxiety at losing fishing time. He doesn't speak unless it is about fishing. He is obsessed, and is pacing up and down and is annoying us. You feel like telling him so.

All the trawlers are dodging and the weather forecast predicts the wind will decrease to gale force and change direction. The wind has been a north-easterly for a while, so it might not be so cold when it changes. The old man can't wait to start fishing again, and he says it's a better weather forecast, so we'll go back on the fishing ground and wait for the wind to drop, in his obsession to start fishing again.

Your watch mates have dared you to take a page out of the sailors' book and tell the old man that he is a stormy b*st*d, in a nice, joking way. He is still pacing up and down in anxiety and you smile at him as best you can and you say, "Why don't you try to relax until the weather fines away because you are stressing yourself out."

The old man hesitates, stone cold, at what you just said, and spins round to face you in a furious rage and shouts, "Do you want to go home without any fish and settle in dept? We are out here to earn a living."

He turns, facing the window, and says we have got to catch some fish because we can't go home with nothing. Steve is looking out the window. Dale has got his head in the radar, and the sparks stayed in the radio room. The bridge stays uncomfortably quiet, and not another word is spoken until the old man leaves. The sparks pops his head round the radio room door with a huge grin on his face, looking highly amused. We all take a breath of fresh air after he has gone. Needless to say, the sailors' way didn't work this time! But, in reality, if a trawler is iced up and got into difficulty in a storm like this, there would be nothing anyone could do to help. To be honest, the trawlers should not be out here at all in this weather. All of the trawlers are dodging back out onto the fishing location one after the other, and they are all ready to shoot if they get the chance.

We are back out, on the fishing grounds, but the wind does not appear to have lost its strength or changed direction, and it is squally with strong gusts. Some of the trawlers even stayed on location to ride out the storm, and they have got seriously iced up. They are dodging up and down, waiting for the weather to calm, and it will be only a matter of time before one of them shoots his trawl in desperation. If one of them does shoot, the rest will follow one by one. The owners' agenda might add that if the trawlers are fishing, the weather must be fine enough to fish in. It could make it difficult for a skipper to use his own discretion, because fishing is a competitive profession, with no rules, and it has a make-or-break outcome, because if a skipper makes a bad trip, he could be sacked, or get a walkabout and put on the dole. There is a daily schedule between the trawlers and the owners which is sent by Morse code, and the owners know what is going on aboard every ship, from their cosy offices.

The lads are in their bunks when the watch comes down from the bridge shouting, "Down trawl lads, all hands." They tell us it is blowing like a b*****d and we're badly iced up. The lads start to chitter and chafe and complain that surely we're not going to shoot in this weather, and someone says, "I'm not coming back aboard here next trip." Everyone else says they're not coming back either. We get our wet gear on and wait until we get to the beginning of the tow and ready for shooting. The watch tells us there is one ship fishing and the old man is following him.

The telegraph rings and we all have our own job to do. We have a strict routine to follow, and we are keeping our fingers crossed for our own safety.

Dale shouts out, "Play smart lads, and watch yourselves." He tells the deckie learner to stay off the deck. This is one of the worst experiences anyone can ever face. It's hard to imagine how a ship and its crew can possibly fish in weather such as this, because it is beyond belief. We are in a living hell, and you don't feel safe at all and, in reality, we are not safe. The only thing you have confidence in is the ship – the brave Arctic Corsair, who has never let us down. When you have sailed in a ship for a while, you begin to know her, and the Corsair is game for anything that is thrown at her. She will take anything on, and she always comes out on top.

We scramble the trawl over the side and ride the waves and heavy swells. We are getting swilled about the deck with a few heart-stopping moments. The winchmen pay the trawl warps away and shout out how many fathoms have gone out until the trawl reaches the bottom, and the afterman shouts, "All square aft." We hope the trawl is catching fish. The old man says we will try to tow for longer if we can find a good tow.

We grab a quick drink and a smoke and start to chop tons of ice off the ship's structure, and the sparks goes on the bridge top to clear the radar scanner and the radio aerials.

Some of the other trawlers are shooting away now, and they are speaking over the air about how bad the weather is, saying it's the worst they have ever seen. We chop ice, and shake the rigging with the Gilson to try to clear the ice off the top. We take our wet gear off and have a breather in the messdeck, and we are all worse for wear. We are facing stress and trauma for twenty-four hours every day. But there are no sissies aboard here. The 60s music helps us to calm our nerves.

The sparks comes to the messdeck and hands a telegram to one of the lads from his wife and family, and everyone goes quiet. All eyes are on the man. He tells us the telegram is from his wife and family, and it says, "We are missing you, come home to us soon". 'Catch the Wind' by Donovan is playing on the tape recorder and the man went to his berth and pinned the telegram in his bunk next to the photograph of his wife and children, with his gold cross hung around them.

The man who had his tooth out is trying to stop the frost from getting into his mouth by covering it with his muffler. It's stopping him from breathing properly and he keeps gasping for breath. And the man with the neck and shoulder injury is struggling to cope. The old man asks, "How are the injured men doing?" But what he really means is: can they work?

We haul and shoot the trawl relentlessly in this terrible weather, day and night for the next two days, and it is soul-destroying. We are all hardened, experienced trawlermen men used to the hardships of fishing in bad weather, but we are feeling the strain because we are risking our lives hauling and shooting the trawl against the howling winds and spray and fighting against the diverse weather conditions. We are lucky to keep getting away with. The weather is not getting any better, and when you are driven to the limit of your endurance, you stop caring, and just carry on.

No matter how bad the weather gets, the seagulls still glide beside us and they are watching us. They do not seem to feel the cold and can survive up to minus 40. They do not get iced up and always look happy. They wait for fish and will eat anything that goes overboard. They go into feeding frenzies, quacking and screeching and fighting with each other with their wings outspread. They fly about in the dark and there is nowhere for them to sleep. Maybe they don't sleep. They have special glands in their throat to divert the salt so they can drink seawater, and they try to swallow things that are bigger than themselves. It looks like they would eat each other if they could, and when it's dark or foggy they know which trawlers are hauling because they can hear the winches. They head towards the sound without vision. It has been said they are the descendants of lost fishermen, but they are more likely the descendants of greedy people who have been sent to limbo.

We are towing along normally when the afterwarp suddenly jumps. It pulls out and is screeching against the brake. We have become fast on the seabed, and the old man stops the engine immediately. Iceland is a volcanic island and there are many fastenings. We knock the towing block out, start the winch up and begin to haul the warps in. We are lucky to come free.

We fight against the weather to get the trawl inboard and, luckily, it is okay, but the nets are partly in shreds, and it is disheartening for us having to mend them in these harsh conditions. We hang the trawl up, and lay it out, and run it down, and we piece it together and start mending it, and men start braiding from different places until they meet up. Sometimes you have to take your gloves off briefly, even though the temperature is below freezing, and someone has to hold the net up to the scan while someone else is mending it. They might wear mittens over their gloves to prevent frostbite.

The old man has got the rum bottle out, and he shouts down from the bridge to come up for a dram. The mood changes for the better, and all our troubles are forgotten. He gives it out in a huge medicine glass, one after the other using the same glass, and some of the lads find it hard to get it down in one go, and they spit it back into the glass, and the old man just throws it out of the window and fills the glass up for the next man. No one complains.

We go back on the deck with a glow-on and someone starts singing and we all join in, but not for long because it soon wears off in the cold. But it does help us.

We go back to fixing the nets and everyone is shouting to the deckie learner for twine and settings, and he is finding it hard to keep the net needles full, and one of the lads goes and helps him. The deckie learner is pale and withdrawn, and he has hardly spoken a word since we left home. The trip is taking it out of him because he is still a child and this is no place for him to be. He should be at home with his mother. But it is said that if you do a trip on a fishing trawler, you will go to sea as a boy and come home as a man. It is part of learning his trade.

One of the lads has got sore hands and wrists because of the constant movement and overuse that causes strain and swelling on his on his fingers and wrist joints (jummies). It is very painful and you can actually hear them creaking. The only cure is to rest them, but no one can rest on a trawler, and he has to carry on working. He is bathing his hands and wrists in the hot cod liver oil boiler to try to put the natural movement and oil back into them.

After an hour or so, the trawl is fixed and we shoot away again. The wind is easing and it has changed direction, which is very encouraging for us. There are twenty baskets of big cod in the pounds which are frozen stiff and we gut them and put them down into the fish room within half an hour. We have been out all night and we are cold and hungry and looking forward to breakfast time. We take our wet gear off and keep our fingers crossed that we are not busted again when we haul. We are fishing on rough ground and the trawl is getting ripped every time we haul and it is causing us hard work and wasting our valuable fishing time. We feel we are getting nowhere.

The breakfast the cook has laid on is a godsend for us, and we forget all our troubles. Food like this is very encouraging and helpful for what's ahead of us.

When we haul, the nets are ripped again, and the bellies are out. The lads are blaming the old man, but he does not give a damn if we blame him or not because he knows the fish is down there and he is taking a chance to find the right tow to catch it. But it is not working. We hang the trawl up, and lay it out, and run the meshes along, and all the lads are mending.

There is an improvement in the weather; the cold wind chill has eased and we are working in better conditions. The Icelandic weather can change at any time. Someone has left an open knife in the rail and a man has put his hand on the blade without knowing it was there. He has cut his finger on it. There are no medics on a trawler, so the man goes in the galley and the cook puts a stitch in it and tapes it up. He is back on the deck within twenty minutes. We are all relieved that he is okay, because it is extra work for us if we're a man short.

The trawl is fixed again and we shoot away. It is dinner time, and it is your watch below from dinner to tea, so you have your dinner second sitting, and after you have your dinner, you and Steve and Dale go to your bunks until teatime. There is roast beef, roast potatoes, mashed potatoes, veg and Yorkshire pudding and a sweet. The cook is the nearest thing you can get to being a mother on a trawler because he feeds you.

Ralph is having his breakfast with us and says he is not enjoying the trip at all because he is not used to this sort of thing. He is frightened, and it is a nightmare for him having to face the weather conditions. He wears his gold cross that Norma bought him and he listens to the 60s music for comfort. You get in your bunk for your watch below just as you are, in your clothes, because you are so tired and there is no time for any routines, and you need every minute's rest you can get. You try to escape from this fishing trawler for a few hours. You fall asleep immediately. You hear them hauling and you know exactly what is going on, because you know every sound and every movement, and you know if things are going right or wrong, and when they shoot away and it goes quiet again. You know things are okay for now!

The weather has improved but it is still a bit unsettled and cold, and we have found a tow without fastenings or mending, and we are catching lots of good, prime fish. When we haul, Dale lets go of the cod ends and you hear a loud thud, and there is a big rock among the fish we have trawled up, maybe weighing half a ton. It could have easily rolled over and broken someone's legs. Or it could have been a wartime bomb or a mine left over from the war that could have exploded. And it does happen. We swing the rock over to the port rail and lash it up, and we will dump it in deep water on our way home, where it can do no harm. We overhaul the trawl because of the rock and there is little damage and we shoot away again and, if the weather allows, we will make up for the time we lost because we have found the fish.

It does not have to be bad weather for accidents to happen, because they can happen at any time, and the next time we haul we are pulling the bellies inboard over the rail. We all pull together and stand on it to stop it pulling back out, and sometimes we have to jump off it quickly if it pulls out unexpectedly. One of the lads has a firm grip on the net with his fingers and he gets pulled over the rail with the bellies, but the lads are there immediately to pull him back inboard, and this happens regularly. But if he had gone into the water, the cold shock of the freezing water would have disorientated him, causing him to panic and breath water into his lungs. He would be in serious danger of secondary drowning even if he was safely inboard, and if one of the lads had gone in to save him, there would be two casualties. And all the lads know that, so we would have to try to grab him with the tommyhawk (an eight-foot pole with a hook at the end) and pull him in with it. But if we get him back inboard, he might still be in serious trouble through not being able to breath because of secondary drowning, with water in his lungs, and we would have to try to clear the water out of his lungs somehow.

# Chapter 8
# The worst ice storm in living memory

It's 26 January 1968. We have been fishing on and off for nearly two weeks and are fatigued. We are taking risks hauling and shooting, and gutting fish and mending nets in the hostile, stormy weather. We are chopping tons of ice off the ship's structure in between. We have an hour to go before hauling time and we are all in the messdeck having a drink and a smoke and trying to unwind the best we can.

The sparks comes in and says, "I have something important to tell you all." He asks if anyone has anyone close to them on board the St Romanus. He tells us she has not been on schedule for fifteen days and one of her life rafts has been found off Flamborough Head. The sparks goes on to say there is a search going on for them and their families have been told. There is little hope for them.

It goes quiet in the messdeck; not a word is said for a while. The fishing communities are close-knit and some of our best mates have been lost with the St Romanus. The lads try to find a conclusion as to what might have happened to her. One of the lads had sailed in her and said she was a bad sea ship and he signed off her. The sparks said the weather at the time was not really bad, and they don't know what could have happened. A loose mine from World War II had been reported to the coastguard in the area, but they couldn't find it.

The shocking news of the loss of the St Romanus has completely taken us over, and the weather conditions here are as bad as they can ever get. We are almost at our limit of endurance. The wind is picking up again and we are icing up fast. The ship is getting heavier and we are chopping ice off the structure all the time.

One of the lads is taking the news of the St Romanus badly. He says his best mate was on her, and he is starting to have panic attacks. It's the worst weather we have been through, and we are still out here fishing in it, when the old man finally decides to get the trawl inboard and go for shelter under the lee of the land. We've got two days fishing time left and the temperature is dropping and the wind is increasing and it looks doubtful if we will shoot again this trip. The man who is having panic attacks could set it off in other members of the crew, and it looks like Ralph could follow him.

The lads have a meeting, and we have all decided we have had enough and want to go home. We call Dale to the messdeck and tell him to go and tell the old man that we want to go home. The old man comes down to the messdeck and says it's the same feeling among all the ship crews – they all want to go home. We have two fishing days left but we will not be fishing any more this trip, and we can start clewing up and getting ready for going home right away. We are just waiting for which market to go for. We stow the trawl down the hold, clear the decks, chop the ice from the ship's structure and batten the hatches. We made the Arctic Corsair shipshape and the engineers trim her up as best as they can.

It's 29 January 1968. Dale is looking pale and worried. He has asked for everyone to come to the messdeck because he has some more bad news to tell us. He asks, "Has anyone got anyone close to them on board the Kingston Peridot?" He tells us one of its life rafts has been washed ashore here at Iceland. The ship has not reported in on her schedule for two days and there are signs of oil being washed ashore along the coast.

Everyone sits in silence. Dale's statement has caused deep shock to us all. One of the lads speaks up and says, "My cousin is in her." The crews of the Kingston Peridot and the St Romanus and their families are known to us. They are part of our lives and our morale is low. We can't take any more. It is not real.

There are thirty or more trawlers taking shelter and talking over the air on their VHF sets, and every one of them has up to 20 tons of ice on their structure above the waterline. Every one of them is in danger of turning over and sinking (just one square metre of water weighs a ton). There is a perfect ice storm going on with giant waves creating ice spray that is being frozen in the air and being carried by the wind over the ships' structures, adding to the weight by the hour, and all we can do to save the ship and our lives is to keep chopping it off as fast as it forms. It would be dangerous to try to run out of it. That is the situation we're in.

It's 1 February 1968 and we are sheltering under the lee of the land in the worst weather any of us has ever seen. We have been carrying out our routine for the safety of the ship for two days. The weather has deteriorated rapidly and there are thirty or more trawlers sheltering from the worst ice storm in living memory. We are working extra hard with all hands to get the Arctic Corsair shipshape to leave our shelter and go out to sea to face the full storm that comes around only once in 100 years. We are preparing to set off for home, and we will be running before the wind in the worst ice storm in living memory.

Ted the engineer is telling the old man it is almost impossible to trim a ship up properly in bad weather with ice on the upper structure, but we can do our best. And pray. Because if we fall into the rough between the waves, beam-on, we would need to be trimmed properly to get out of it, and especially running before the wind.

The Arctic Corsair has a powerful Mirrlees Monarch engine backed up by two turbines and a powerful thruster towing screw designed for speed, power and reliability. She will not stop for anything. She can get over the highest waves with ease! Sometimes she nearly takes off in getting over them. She will leave you in mid-air as she crashes down into the troughs. She is seemingly getting excited, and is always raring to go. She will be pushed along with the mountainous seas behind her and passing her, with her engines racing to the limit.

The old man shouts for the watch on the bridge and you, Steve and Dale are on watch. Our hearts are pounding and our nervous channels are stretched to the limit.

You take your wet gear off and hang it up in the drying room, and go up to the bridge where the old man is making final preparations with the sparks in the radio room.

Before we set off, Ralph comes onto the bridge to see what's going on. He is terrified. We encourage him and reassure him that he will be okay. The old man gives him a co-codamol. It's the wonder pill fishermen are told will cure everything, and stop him from being frightened. The old man tells Ralph this pill will last for twenty-four hours, and we will be out of the storm and in fine weather when it wears off.

The old man shouts to the lads to get off the deck and batten down as we prepare to leave the safety of the lee of the land and try to run out of the storm. We encourage Ralph to give his Swiss maid yodel out of the bridge window at the storm in his high, perfect-pitch Welsh soprano voice. "Yololo, laydyeeee. Yololo, laydeeee". We're going home, and the crew stop chopping the ice with axes, with their beards covered in frost, and yodel the song along with him in their defiance.

We are running before the storm with mountainous seas following us. We are being carried along as if on a surfboard and the white tops are catching us up and passing us, because the seas are running faster than the ship. You are at the wheel and struggle to keep the ship on course and under control. The stern goes up with the wave and the bow races down it. The ship starts to twist and turn as the waves race by. The compass is swinging and swaying and whizzing back and forth. You keep the rudder indicator ten degrees over to port to bring her back on course. The decks are full of water, then you wait for the next wave coming and hope it isn't as big as the last one. Most seamen don't like to run before the wind, because the sea takes control of the ship, and the seas could easily overwhelm you. This type of weather has been experienced by every seaman. Sometimes you hear fools bragging about how brave they are, but you should always respect the sea, because a wave can reach a mile high, and travel at 500 mph, faster than a jet plane, and can destroy everything in its path. It only takes a landslide or an earthquake or a meteor and the nice, calm sea the idiots mocked and played on will soon show how powerful it really is. They might not live to tell the tale.

Steve is on lookout on the port wing. He cleans the salt from the bridge windows and switches the lights off. Dale is at the radar, and you are at the wheel. The weather forecast gives out a northerly, severe, full storm force twelve imminent. This is another piece of cruel news for us to cope with. The wind is in the same direction that we're in now. You have to hold on as the ship lies over and shudders as a huge wave races past, filling the starboard side and the foredeck with water and laying us over. The ship is being carried to wherever the next wave takes us and it is hard to keep on course.

Steve relieves you at the wheel. You give him the course, and he repeats it after you. Dale tells you to go down and check that the doors and potholes are battened down properly. You struggle to get down off the bridge. You have to time your movements along the alleyway to the messdeck. The crew are sat around fully dressed lounging on the seat lockers, rather than get in their bunks, because the movement of the ship is so aggressive. You check on Ralph and the deckie learner, who are with the cook in his berth opposite the messdeck. The door is left open, and the chief engineer is sat in his berth next door. The situation is concerning. You go round jamming things up and check the doors and the portholes. The wind is on the port quarter behind us and at times the ship lies over to starboard and shudders, and then she lies over to port on the bigger waves, and your instincts are urging the ship to come back up and keep steady. No one can sleep and the lads are staying alert, hoping we will soon run out of it.

You put your finger through three half-filled mugs of tea and keep one hand for yourself and perform a balancing act. You struggle to get back to the bridge without spilling any. Your watch mates are glad of a cup of tea, or what's left of it. They ask you what the situation is down there. You tell them the lads are lying about in the messdeck and the others are sat in their berths until we run out of it. The cook has left food out if anyone wants it.

We are going through a tense time and are still heavy with ice build-up on the high structure where we can't reach. The old man keeps showing his face on the bridge and showing his concern about the squally full storm warning ahead of us. Things could not be worse for us. Two of our ships and their crews have gone missing and thirty or more of our trawlers are top heavy with ice. The lads are chopping it off as fast as it forms. The Arctic

Corsair's crew are fighting for survival in a full storm leaving Iceland.

We don't talk much. We have to think positively and be prepared for anything that could happen. We tell the old man what a nervous state Ralph is in and he says he will go down and speak with him when he gets the chance. He says, "My wife will never forgive me if anything happens to Ralph."

The situation with the ships sheltering at Iceland is that if the storm does not stop soon, all thirty could be in danger of being lost one by one because of the ice build-up, and there is nothing anyone can do about it. But, unbelievably, there are more trawlers on their way to Iceland's fishing grounds to join them.

It's 6.30 p.m. and it's teatime. The next watch take over from us on the bridge and they are not happy with the weather conditions. Dale tells them to call the old man out if there is any further build-up of ice, but it is unlikely now because we are sailing before the wind and not making any ice spray. The old man is hanging around and keeps showing his face on the bridge. Dale tells the watch about the severe storm warning and they say surely it can't get any worse than it is now.

We go down to the mess deck and join the lads. The cook has made sandwiches but we have lost our appetite. Our thoughts are with the two ships and what could have happened to them. You think of the families and what the mood is like in Hull and Hessle Road. You think that sometimes you will run out of the worst part of a storm like this in a short time. Let us hope that, because we are going through a living nightmare. Stress and trauma is a modern disease invented by sissies, but there is none of that here. We just have to get on with it.

The worst of the storm comes around midnight and early morning. Everyone except the watch and the engineers are in the messdeck, or sat in their berths. The safest thing we can do for the safety of the ship, and for our own safety, is to head into the storm at slow speed and dodge it out. But we are on a Hull fishing trawler heading for home, with a thousand kits of fish in the hold, and we are racing to catch the market, and this old man and the Arctic Corsair will not stop for anything.

The next morning at breakfast the weather is still very bad, but the worst is behind us and the lads are in the messdeck. The ship is racing along and lying over and shuddering heavily. We are being pushed along by the wind and seas, and the engines are changing pitch and racing at full speed. The old man will not ease her in for anything, but our speed and engine revs have to be governed to match the state of the running seas, for safety. It is impossible for the cook to prepare breakfast, because you can't stand up without holding on, and you need both hands for yourself. He has left a cold buffet out for us. The Arctic Corsair will throw you to the side, or in the air, or throw you in any direction and leave you on your knees if you don't hold on. The galley is a bad place to be in bad weather, and boiling water and hot food can be thrown off the stove at you. The ship is steadier now and we feel a lot safer, but she is still racing and lying over.

It's 12.30 p.m., dinner time. The cook has made a pan of stew and some sandwiches. It's amazing how he has done it.

Some of the older hands say it's the worst trip they have done and they will be glad to get home, and Ralph and the deckie learner must have gone through the worst traumatic experience they will never forget. The trip they did to Iceland's North Cape in 1968 could put an end to their fishing careers.

You, Steve and Dale go to the bridge and take over the watch. The weather is better and the ship is steadier but it is still bad, and the lads have all turned into their bunks, exhausted. You are on lookout on the port side and Steve is on the wheel. Dale is watching the radar. The old man has come to the bridge still wearing his fishing jersey. He speaks to us about the St Romanus, and the Kingston Peridot, and about the crews and their families. He tells us there is a massive Hessle Road and dockland vigil, with hundreds of people gathered. He tells us the weather is still very bad at Iceland, and all the ships are still sheltering and chopping ice.

The sparks comes on the bridge and tells us the latest weather forecast is giving out easterly winds, force five to six, for this area ahead of us. The weather forecast is a relief, because we have been living on our nerves for so long. Steve goes down to check around and tells the lads the weather is going to get better, and it is getting better all the time, and Ralph is there listening, wide-eyed and looking pale, and it is welcoming news for us all.

We have left the Iceland behind us and are heading towards the North Sea. The wind has come round to force four five in a southerly direction on our bow, and the sea state is acceptable. The daymen open the doors and go out on the deck and do what jobs they can. The lads are unwinding from the stressful time they have gone through and things are beginning to get back to normal. The 60s music is sounding out and the ship is much steadier. Ralph is showing colour in his face again after going through the worst storms and zero temperatures that anyone can remember. The tragic news of our two ships and their crews that are missing has left its mark on all of us. This trip has been a terrible ordeal, physically and mentally, and not only aboard the Arctic Corsair, but for all the ships' men who are out here.

The ice has gone from our structure and the air is warmer. It is getting lighter and the storm has pushed us nearer to home with its wind speed, and we are in good time to catch the morning tide for

Tuesday's market. The sparks tell us that the storm in Iceland has passed and the ships are back out fishing again. Our lads are playing crib and canasta in the messdeck to pass the time with the music on.

It's Sunday 4 February 1968. We are in the North Sea approaching Flamborough Head. The wind is south-west, force five. The Arctic Corsair is racing towards the Spurn lightship, which is anchored 5 miles seaward from the entrance of the River Humber. The lads have hoisted a new red ensign peacetime flag at the stern of the ship at half-mast in tribute to the tragic news of our two ships that are missing. Everyone is cleaning and packing their gear ready for docking on the next morning's tide, and the shore gear is hanging out ready to go ashore. Ralph has his three-day millionaire suit hung up ready. He has got the teatime pots out of the way and has finished his work for the trip. We are docking at 9 a.m.

We are approaching the River Humber, going home, and our nerves are settling down after our ordeal when suddenly Dale sends for all hands to go to the messdeck right away. Dale says, "Is everyone here? Because there is some more bad news to tell you. I don't know how to tell you this, but has anyone got someone close to them on board the Ross Cleaveland?"

Those words hit home straight away.

Dale says, "She has turned over and sunk with all hands while sheltering from the storm." He had tears in his eyes, and the news is too much for the lads to take. We are in deep shock. This cannot be happening. Our friends and family members are being lost at sea one after the other. We have lost three trawlers and sixty of our friends and relations and shipmates in the space of three weeks. The toughest men from everywhere have tears in their eyes, and all we want to do is go home to be with our families.

We sail round Spurn lightship and drop anchor at Killingholme anchorage and get our number for the market and wait until the next morning's tide for the signal for us to pull our anchor and go down the 25-mile journey to St Andrew's Dock.

You play cards for a while, but you give up because your mind and thoughts are elsewhere.

# Chapter 9

We are the crew of the Arctic Corsair and we are anchored at Killingholme in the River Humber. We are waiting for the morning tide to take us down river to Hull's sacred lock gates to land our fish. We have made it home through the worst storm in Iceland's living memory – it was a storm that only comes around only once in every 100 years. Three Hull trawlers and fifty-eight crewmen have been lost at sea within three weeks of each other. The storm lasted for fifteen hours at its worst and thirty trawlers had taken shelter under the lee of the land, getting iced up by the combination of freezing sea sprays and snow that was being kicked up by the storm. If the storm had not stopped when it did, after fifteen hours, every one of the ships would have been in danger of turning over with the weight of the ice build-up.

The loss of our fellow shipmates, and working through the terrible storm, has taken it out of our crew, who are among the toughest men in the world. But this trip to Iceland has left its mark on us all.

It's 7 a.m. on 4 February 1968 and we are waiting for permission to pull anchor and make the 25-mile journey down the River Humber to Hull's St Andrew's sacred lock gates. The River Humber is by no means a safe river to sail on. It has a swirling six-knot tide and shifting sandbanks and the ships that are not familiar with it need a river pilot to guide them down it. Some people refer to the River Humber as "the river of no return" because of its reputation – 6,000 Hull fishermen and 900 ships from Hull alone! And many ships and crews from Grimsby sailed up this river and were never seen again. There has never been much publicity given out about the River Humber's secret notoriety, or about the thousands of men and ships that have been taken down to the sea on its tides, never to be seen again. And in reality the River Humber has a far greater, proven reputation for creating indirect disasters than the Bermuda Triangle. The Bermuda Triangle stories are a made up of myth for American publicity to gain tourism. But the Bermuda Triangle cannot nearly match the River Humber for its true statistics.

It's 8 a.m. and Killingholme anchorage are signalling for us to pull anchor and proceed down the river to Hull. We will be there about 10 a.m. The lads are making final touches in preparation for going ashore and putting their shore gear on and the old man and Dale and the third hand are on the bridge. The old man knows the river with no problem, and so does Dale. We pass Easington oil terminal to starboard and Grimsby tower to port. There is a lot of traffic on the river, and the North Sea Ferries are coming down at speed, so we have to watch ourselves. The tide is coming in behind us, carrying us down the river on our way home.

The old man and the crew are nervous about going home to meet the Hull and Hessle Road community waiting on the quays that have come to meet their loved ones. We feel a bit guilty and don't know how to act. Our nervous channels start to kick in.

We pass the corporation pier, see the Bullnose and the green for go is showing, so we can go alongside. We swing round at the Bullnose and head for the insurance buildings quay and throw our ropes ashore. There are lots of people gathered on the quays and the Bullnose and the quays around the lock gates are covered in bouquets of flowers and wreaths and some of the people are down on their knees in grief at the news of their lost loved ones. There are other trawlers behind us coming home one by one. The families of the crews are meeting them in and waiting for them on the quayside. Ralph's girlfriend Norma and her mother have come to meet him in and he steps onto the quay.

Lilly Bilocca, Christine, Mary and Yvonne are down the dock waiting to confront the trawler owners about the safety on board at sea. They are being escorted by the police. We pass through the lock gates to the fish market and make way for the ship coming in behind us and tie up. The old man rings "Finished with Engines", and our taxis are waiting to take us home.

In the taxi, you realise how overtired and exhausted you are. The trip has taken it out of you, and you know your body needs lots of rest, but your mind is not yet ready for it, so you arrange to meet Steve in Rayners later because you need to talk to your friends.

The neighbours are watching from behind the curtains and on their doorsteps and the kids stop playing to watch you get out of the taxi. They watch your family greet you at the door. You need to sit down and relax for a while to catch up. Your wife asks if you're okay, saying you look tired and withdrawn. You say you just need to rest for an hour or so. She runs you a bath and puts your clothes out for you. She says you need to lie down after your bath and sleep for a while. You relax in the bath, get dressed and ring Steve. He tells you he has had a beer and feels tired but needs to go out, and you agree to meet in Rayners. You think to yourself that you don't need much to drink.

You meet Steve and he tells you Dale is on his way to meet us. Rayners is full, as usual, and Hessle Road is in shock. The whole of Hull is in mourning and the atmosphere is terrible. The *Hull Daily Mail* says there are many things the four protest ladies including Lilly Bilocca are demanding to know from the trawler owners. They are asking what happened? How did it happen?

Could it have been prevented? Why is it that only the Hull trawlers are being lost?

Dale says the crew need a day or two longer at home this trip to recover. We have another wintry trip ahead of us in February, but I doubt if any of the crew will go back next trip. We will see when we go down to settle tomorrow. I will talk to the owners about it, but it's very unlikely they will agree.

You go to the bar to get the beer in and Shiela the barmaid comes over and serves you straight away. She asks if you have you been to Iceland and you say yes. Shiela is an outstanding barmaid. The landlady is busy serving too and gives you a nod. They are used to serving fast because the pub is always full, every day. You carry the beer back to your table and can see the people passing by the pub's window on Hessle Road. You think of what is in their thoughts, and do they have anyone close connected to these terrible tragedies. You see Ralph and Norma walking by and Steve goes out and gives them a shout. Women are not appreciated in Rayners bar, or in any of the bars in the pubs on Hessle Road. Steve leads them to the side entrance into the back room. The room is big and holds concerts every afternoon and night. We take our drinks into the back room and manage to get a table. Ralph says it's nice to be home, but I'm still shaking with fear. Norma said she and her mam don't want Ralph to go back fishing any more!

Norma has been hearing stories from the fishermen living in the mission and said she wants Ralph to get a job at home.

Dale says he can see the deckie learner at the far end of the room with his family and he's got a pint in front of him. You and Ralph go across to talk, while Dale and Steve speak to Norma. You know the deckie learner's family and his mother. She asks how he coped out there, and you say he coped very well, he is a real tough guy, and his brothers laugh. His mother says she doesn't want him to go back any more and doesn't like him drinking and smoking and doing what he wants. He's only 16, but how can you stop him when he does a job like that? The deckie learner's family are glad to meet Ralph and are interested in what he has to say, because he always gives it out exactly as things happened.

We go back to our table and Ralph says he is not going back to sea ever again. Norma says she is going to help him to find a job ashore. Their music is playing in the background, and it is a very pleasant and relaxing atmosphere.

The doors open and a commotion starts. Lilly, Christine, Yvonne and Mary have come in and they have been speaking to the trawler owners to protest about the safety conditions aboard. They said they watched us come through the lock gates on the Arctic Corsair this morning. The landlady finds them some seats and Steve gets them a drink. The four ladies make a pledge to bring changes for the safety of fishermen at sea. The landlady comes to join Lilly and Christine. Ralph tells Mary and Yvonne about the weather conditions in Iceland and they are very concerned about it. Christine leans over to you and emotionally says, "Did you know that our Phil was the skipper of the Ross Cleveland?" You say yes, you know, and you are very sorry. She says we must bring in some safety regulations after this, and they have arranged to speak to all the trawler owners about it.

A girl comes to the table asking if you saw the Prince Charles at Iceland, because her dad is on it. You tell her all the ships are fine and sheltered from the weather. You try to reassure her, even though you don't know yourself. It is dark in Iceland in the winter months and you cannot identify another ship; you can only see its lights.

Lilly, Christine, Mary and Yvonne have had a busy day and are moving on. You, Steve and Dave need some sleep.

But, suddenly, the atmosphere in the pub changes and the news comes through that the mate of the Ross Cleveland, Harry Eddom, has survived and two crewmen have died in a life raft. Harry is in hospital in Iceland, but we don't know any more until it's made official.

# Chapter 10

It's 5 February 1968 and the incredible survival story of the mate of the Ross Cleveland, Harry Eddom, being washed ashore in a life raft is the main headline across all the newspapers. The story in the *Hull Daily Mail* says he was the mate of the Ross Cleveland when it sank and he was out in the storm on top of the bridge fully dressed in his duck suit, clearing the ice from the radar scanner when the ship turned over. The other two crew members were not properly dressed but managed to launch a life raft and get aboard it, but sadly they died from exposure. If the two men had been wearing warm clothing and their duck suits, it might have saved their lives, but there was not enough time for them to go to the drying room to get properly dressed. The life raft would have been flooded with icy water and would need to be inflated and bailed out in impossible conditions. The wind blew the life raft ashore after twelve hours and Harry Eddom was found at a farmyard by a shepherd and taken to hospital. It is an incredible story of survival.

The next morning, you feel fatigued. You were catnapping all night but you're okay. You put your old gear on, ready to go down to the fish market to watch your fish being sold. You watch out for the tally switchers who steal fish and for the quality control who will condemn good fish to supply the trawler owners' fishmeal and pet food factory, leaving some poor fisherman to settle in dept after risking his life to catch it.

Steve picks you up at 6.30 a.m. The fish market is noisy, everyone is busy and the auctioneers are shouting and bobbers are walking about in their four-inch-high wooden clogs with studs to stop them from slipping. You think all bobbers are six feet or over and very noisy people and you keep out of their way. Dale is there giving out fish passes to our crew, to show the police at the gate you are not stealing it. Dale gives you and Steve a glass of rum. Fish is very scarce today and the prices are sky high. You and Steve are keeping watch on your fish. The quality control bandits are walking in your direction and they spot you watching them, so they leave your fish alone.

The Arctic Corsair has landed her catch once more and she will be ready to sail again in two days. You go back home and take your clothes off at the door; if the smell of fish gets into your house, you will never get rid of it. You get straight into the bath and unwind for a while.

It's 5 February and is settling day. Steve and his wife come to your house for a drink before we go down to settle. We try to keep our minds on the day and hope we don't hear any more bad news. We have to decide if we are going back to sea in the Arctic Corsair this trip. Steve says it would be nice

121

if they gave us a couple of days extra at home. The girls are worried, but we have to make a decision before we go down to the office. Shall we sail or sign off the Arctic Corsair? If we sign off and go in another ship, it won't make the weather any better, so we best stay with the Arctic Corsair. Steve agrees straight away. The girls show their concern, but they have seen this situation before and reluctantly go along with it.

You and Steve go into the ship's runner's office. The Arctic Corsair's log book is open on his desk with a pen lying beside it. The runner asks, "Are you going back in the Arctic Corsair this trip?" He has an uncertain look on his face. Steve says yes and signs his name in the log book, then shoves the pen into your hand. The ship's runner smiles and says you are ordered for Friday the 9th at 5 a.m. and the automatic steering is completed for you this trip.

We go upstairs to the settling office and have done well, because the markets are high due to the scarcity of fish. A few of the crew, the cook, Ralph and the deckie learner sit waiting for the pay hatch to open. Some of the crew have signed off to have a few days at home to unwind. The cook is a leader of men and he is going back. The tough little Yorkie is going back too, against his mother's wishes. Ralph has signed off to look for a better and safer life. The crew have arranged to meet in town in the Regent. You treat Ralph well and wish him all the best. He says he will take Norma in town later and we say yes, we look forward to seeing you. We get in the taxi, drive past the Bullnose and the sacred gates, then clang over the swing bridge and past the Marr and Lord Line buildings and down through the railway tunnel. We turn right past the Fishermen's Mission and head for town along the bankside.

We're in the Regent pub. The locals call it big Regent, because it is a big pub. We have just landed on the Arctic Corsair and have an extra day at home for the automatic steering to be completed. Most of the crew have signed off to rest after going through the worst weather in living memory in Iceland. Steve gets the drinks in and we find a suitable table. Dale and his wife come in and join us. The wives are all pals and love to get together on settling day – they don't stop talking all day. The cook and his wife come and join us and he says he's been speaking to Ralph about going back in the Arctic Corsair and has asked the ship's runner to hold the galley boy's job for a day for Ralph in case he changes his mind. The old man and his wife come in followed by Ralph and Norma. We pull some tables together for them. The old man says we are going back to Iceland, they've fixed the automatic steering and we've got an extra day ashore. Ralph has been pulled straight into the ladies' conversation and is telling them about the Icelandic weather to get it off his chest. He has the full

123

audience listening, because of his honest personality, with Norma listening beside him.

We speak to Ralph about going back in the Arctic Corsair. The cook is talking to him very convincingly and Norma is listening. The old man says the weather in Iceland is caused by the position of the jet stream bringing the weather down from the north and the warm waters of the Gulf Stream, and when it moves the weather will get better. The old man says he has done a trip in February once with hardly a breath of wind, and we all had to agree on that, because we've seen it happen. After this trip the weather should get better as the months pass and the summer comes in, and it will get lighter until the sun is shining for twenty-four hours a day with hardly any darkness at all in Iceland.

The cook tells Ralph his job is there for him if he wants it and he has left it open for him to decide. Ralph sits quietly, and so does Norma. All eyes are on him and he turns to the ladies for advice but they want him to decide and talk it over with Norma. We spend the rest of the afternoon drinking and talking and trying to get things back to normal. The old man says jokingly to his wife, "Are we going to Carver's fish restaurant for fish and chips, love!?" She does not answer him, and we all laugh.

The next day you get a chance to relax and sort things out like a haircut and getting the things you need to take with you, not forgetting to buy your bottle and a case.

Harry Eddom's name is on the headline of every newspaper, telling of his incredible story of survival. You have known Harry all your life and it upsets you a lot – you hope he is okay because he's a smashing bloke.

The Hull and Hessle Road communities are in shock and the media are reporting that four ladies – Lilly Bilocca, Christine Jensen, Mary Denness and Yvonne Blenkinsop – have arranged for an interview with the trawler owners over the safety of the fishermen at sea. They have said enough is enough, and they are protesting at the St Andrew's sacred gates under police escort. They are stopping the ships from sailing if they are not fully crewed with a radio operator on board. The four ladies have spoken with the trawler owners and Prime Minister Harold Wilson about safety at sea.

Why is it that only the Hull trawlers are being lost and not so many from the other ports?

Steve rings and tells you Ralph has been down to the office and has signed back on the Arctic Corsair. You smile and think to yourself what a character Ralph is, and what a character the tough little Yorkie is too.

# Chapter 11
## Iceland after the storm

It's Friday 9 February 1968 and the Arctic Corsair and her crew are preparing to go back fishing at Iceland after witnessing the worst storm in living memory. It was a once-in-100-year ice spray storm that no one will ever forget, and you are not at all happy about going back there.

You go through your same routine. You put on a brave smile for your family and pick up your bag and walk out to the taxi where your shipmates are waiting. It's 6 a.m. and it's cold and dark. The taxi pulls away from your door and you take a long look back. The mood is quiet on the way down to the ship.

The taxi pulls up at the front of the Lord Line building where the Arctic Corsair is waiting as you get out of the taxi and get your gear aboard. You can smell fresh paint, the engine is idling and the generators are whining. You go to the stores and glance at the warning notice on the pumphouse wall saying it is an offence to take alcohol aboard trawlers. You think, *whoever wrote that notice has never been to sea.* We have a can and a dram or two and it is comforting. The ship's runner shouts out everyone ashore who is going ashore and the telegraph rings for the standby to let go. The ropes are thrown off the bollards, and the Arctic Corsair goes slowly astern and then ahead slowly through the sacred gates of St Andrew's.

It's 8 a.m. and it's dark and cold but there are lots of people and police on the quay. The four ladies of the Fishermen's Safety Charter are on the quay, fighting for the safety of fishermen. The police sent a 7-stone female officer to take control of Lilly, but she is 17 stone, so they sent ten extra policemen and still did not control her. The four ladies are making their point, shouting enough is enough and asking how many more Hull trawlers and crews will be lost without safety precautions in place. They are shouting up at the bridge, asking if there is a radio man on board. The sparks showed himself on the bridge veranda and says, "Yes, I'm here!" They give our crew a wave, and shout "All the best lads" and "Take care of yourselves" as we sail through of the lock gates. The old man rings her on and the powerful engines churn the water up and we are on our way. We look back at the scene of the Bullnose the lock gates, the quays, the buildings and you get the loneliest feeling that you are leaving your home and loved ones behind.

We batten the hatches, secure the ship and have a can and a dram. The cook and Ralph are putting the stores away and the engineers are sorting the engine room out. There is the smell of diesel and vegetables and paint in the air. The Arctic Corsair's engines are going full ahead and she is raring to go.

The cook comes into the berth and we give him a dram and Ralph refuses and says he can't stand the smell of it. He has got over the seasickness now after doing four trips, but he tells us he is frightened of going through the bad weather like we did last trip. The deckie learner sits there with a can of lager in his hand without a care in the world, even though he is only 16. You have unpacked your tape recorder and you give it to Ralph to put on the shelf in the messdeck. He says yes, he will do that right away and the music helps him a lot to cope.

We sail round the Spurn lightship on our port side and take a U-turn to a northerly course and the wind is force four on our port quarter, just right. You, Steve and Dale are on watch at dinner until teatime. The automatic steering is set up, so we don't have to steer, but we still have to look out. You're on the port wing, Steve is standing behind the wheel and Dale is on the radar. The thing bothering us now is if the weather at Iceland has improved, because it will be hard for us to do another trip like the last trip. Some of the lads that stayed at home were pressured by their wives and children to stay there until the weather gets better. Fishing communities worry about their men when they are at sea, even in the summer. Dale says it would be nice if it's fine weather and we catch a trip and get back home quickly. I did a trip like that once and it was February. It was flat calm all the way, there and back. We'll ask the sparks if he's heard anything when he comes on the bridge.

We do the usual field day and dish the bond out and make the most of the fine weather and have a laugh and a can and a dram until dinner time. Then you, Steve and Dale are on watch again from dinner to teatime. The automatic steering is working well and will free you and Steve up if something occurs The sparks comes out of the radio room, where he also sleeps, and tells us he has briefly heard that most of the ships are fishing and the weather has improved since we left. The weather ahead is moderate, with no gale warning given out as yet.

You go down to the galley to make the tea and the lads are in their bunks. Ralph and the cook are tidying up with the 60s music playing and you tell them the good news about the weather ahead. Ralph smiles. They have just prepared a cold supper for early morning watch.

Ralph is keeping a diary and you ask him what he has written in it. You are shocked into reality when he reads it out to you: "I have only been a fisherman for four months and I nearly died with seasickness on my first trip on board of the Arctic Corsair in a force-eight gale. And then the ship collided with another ship called Olive in thick fog and we were taking in water and sinking, but no help came because of the thick fog. We made a touch-and-go dash to beach her at Sinclair's Bay.

The rescue party came and took us to a posh hotel and they flew us back to Hull the next day and I had never flown on a plane before. The ship's runner put me in the Fishermen's Mission and I stayed there until I signed on the Arctic Buccaneer, with the same skipper and crew. We went fishing at Russia and the Russian navy came and fired blanks and threatened to sink us. There was a warship and a submarine, and a helicopter with a man waving from the doorway for us to leave. I saw the Northern Lights flickering in the sky but I have never heard of them before. I did two trips in the Arctic Buccaneer, and we all stayed home for Christmas and I met Norma and her mam. And after new year we sailed for Iceland back on the Arctic Corsair. And I have never been so frightened or upset when the three Hull trawlers sank in the worst storm in living memory, and all the ships went for shelter. I was terrified when I was told we were going to make a dash for home through the hurricane and we got home safely, and we joined in with the Hull community's sorrow and grief when we tied up at the quay, and everyone was crying and even the crew of the Arctic Corsair were all in tears. And now as I am writing in my diary we are back in Iceland with a new Fisherman's Safety Charter to help us. Is it possible for anyone to go through so much as I have done in just four months!"

You take the tea to the bridge. The old man is out and you tell the watch what Ralph has just read out to you from his diary. It leaves us pondering the reality of being a fisherman, and what can happen to us. The old man says jokingly, "Just wait till Ralph tells the wives about this in the pub when we get home."

The sparks hands the old man some information that has come through, and he takes some time looking at it. He says he has received a message from the trawler owners saying the Fishermen's Safety Charter report from the government says all trawler skippers must make the safety of the ship and men the top priority. Eighty-eight measures have been brought in. The old man reads it and put it down, then picks it up and reads it again and again. He takes it with him to the chart room. The four ladies that stood protesting on the quay have certainly changed the game for the safety of ships and men the world over and will save many lives.

At breakfast the next morning the crew talk about the legislation that has passed through parliament so quickly, within one day. It is so important to have health and safety regulations at sea, the same as they have in every other industry, and it makes so much sense. These four heroic ladies have stood up and challenged the trawler owners and the government and they challenged the idiots who opposed them. They had death threats, lost their jobs and were harassed by the police everywhere they went. They even spent their own money for the cause and were never compensated for it.

The next day, the sparks comes onto the bridge with an added version of the Fishermen's Safety Charter and passes it to the old man. He took a long time reading it and said the government have brought in eighty-eight measures immediately. A mother ship will be put on station in the fishing grounds of Iceland with updated medical and radio facilities. The Fishermen's Safety Charter has laid the foundations for generations to come and will save many lives and ships.

There has been little fanfare for these ladies. They have not been recognised for their achievements and their combined determination. They are unsung heroes who saved many lives through their actions. These four safety ladies formed a sisterhood in the Hull and Hessle Road fishing community and changed the dangers the Hull fishermen had to face. How many fathers, husbands, brothers, sons and families and friends were saved because of the legislation these four great ladies laid down for us? How many families would look different or not exist at all if it wasn't for these four ladies? The ladies planned to picket Harold Wilson's home with a 10,000-name petition and were given an appointment with him and the government. The ministers granted every one of their requests. The fishing heritage community are very proud of their assets and guard them with pride, and we want the government to give these four ladies proper recognition.

# Chapter 12
## Safety at last

The Fishermen's Safety Charter has been laid down by the British government and the crews are delighted at the news, but a little worried they will take safety too far and be politically correct to the extent of stopping us earning a living. The line has to be drawn somewhere, and to be honest, a fisherman's life is dangerous at the best of times. The old man says that before we sailed, the owners sent for him in the office and told him to be extra weather-conscious this trip because of the government intervention. But whether the old man takes any notice of the legislation or not remains to be seen.

The sparks says the ships are fishing at Iceland but they are still icing up with wind spray and sub-zero temperatures. There is a gale warning imminent, which is normal for this time of the year. We still have a day's steam ahead of us to get there.

We are heading into a north-east Icelandic gale and are starting to ice up. We are a day away from the fishing grounds, the Arctic Corsair is steaming full and she is kicking ice spray over her structure, but we have to make headway. The only alternative is to ease the engines down to half speed and zigzag the course to prevent icing up so much, but it will add a day to our journey, meaning a day's less fishing time and money being wasted for the expedition.

The old man is silent and starts to pace up and down in thought. You, Steve and Dale are looking out through the windows wondering if the old man will abide by the new Fisherman's Safety Charter laws or just carry on as he has always done. We are steadily icing up and it would be wise to stop and get rid of the ice before we carry on again, but the old man says nothing and carries on as if he hasn't noticed it. Then he decides to zigzag, still going full ahead, but it doesn't work; we are still icing up and he realises he must slow down to half speed and dodge it out. He still does not stop to chop the ice off and he is not following the safety at sea charter laws.

The sparks came from the radio room and says the gale has picked up on the fishing grounds and some of the ships have stopped fishing and are dodging it out. We are all watching the old man's actions, but he just stands looking out of the window as though he didn't hear, or didn't want to hear.

It's teatime and we change watches. We are zigzagging at half speed to prevent ice build-up and some of the ships have stopped fishing in gale-force winds. We go down for tea and the cook and Ralph are busy at the stove. Ralph is learning to cook and has prepared the tea under the cook's instructions and he's very proud. He is still worried about the bad weather, but we tell him not to worry because we have to follow the new safety rules. We tell him how nice the meal is and if he keeps doing this and sits for his cook's ticket, he will be a fully-fledged trawler cook on full pay in no time.

It's dinner time the next day and it is watch time for you, Steve and Dale. It's dark and hostile, the same kind of weather as when we left last trip. We are approaching the fishing grounds and your nervous channels are starting to kick in. You, Steve and Dale are on the bridge and the old man is pacing up and down and getting on your nerves. No one is speaking. We are looking out the windows into the darkness and can see the lights of the other trawlers flickering in the distance. The wind is howling and the sea state is rough. More of the ships have stopped fishing now and they are dodging the weather out.

The old man rings the telegraph down to slow and says to Dale, "We will have to hang around until the weather gets better before we can shoot. I'm going down to have a quick bite to eat." He leaves the bridge. We are dumbstruck with disbelief because we would normally be risking our lives to get the trawl over this side and start fishing. The four ladies have really made their point clear. The safety legislation is being carried out and many lives will be saved for generations to come. We must be sure the four ladies get the recognition they deserve with a proper title to their name. The old man is following the safety laws, and life aboard the Arctic Corsair and every trawler is much safer.

The old man waits for the other trawlers to shoot first, and he gets the trawl aboard and tied up at the first sign of any bad weather. He proceeds with caution and safety, along with the rest of the trawler fleet.

It's 15 February 1968. We are back on location on Iceland's fishing grounds, just three weeks after the worst storm and adverse weather conditions in living memory. The storm has shaken up the fishing industry with a new era of safety laws. But we are still wondering if the old man will abide by the new legislation or not.

Steve brings the tea on the bridge and the old man comes back up and starts pacing up and down, annoying everybody, and the sparks comes in and says all the ships have got their gear aboard and they are all dodging the weather and taking shelter and chopping ice at every opportunity. We are losing time and money, but we can do nothing but wait for fine weather to come.

We talk about the things that matter to us, and Steve says after going through the experience of what happened last trip, it would have been nice if the trawler owners had given us a few days at home to get over it. The sparks is always there to get a good conversation going. It is amazing how the owners can land the fish and get the trawler back to sea in such a short time. The trawler owners are forcing the fishermen back to sea for up to ten and eleven months of the year, away from home after spending only a few days at home with their families. They would like the ships to stay away at sea catching fish all the time. The fishermen are pushed to their maximum capacity, and there is no limit to what the trawler owners expect from them. The trawler owners have no concern for the fishermen or their families, and they do not even have any health and safety guidelines in place. The fishermen go to sea to earn their living and keep the network going, and the fish we take home keeps people in work. Without the fish to process, there would be a great loss of jobs in the UK.

The conversation leaps from one subject to another, and even back to the war before any of us were born, when the British government relied on the country's fishermen to catch fish to feed the nation through two world wars. Only two out of three of the trawlers ever came back home, because the Germans were waiting to blow them up and sink them, and hundreds of fishermen from Hull and Grimsby and other fishing ports lost their lives. The wartime communities sang a tribute to them, along with the soldiers losing their lives for the cause:

"Oh there won't be many coming home
No there won't be many coming home

No there won't be many
Maybe five, maybe twenty
But there won't be many coming home!"

But the trawlers still sailed and brought fish home, because the people of Great Britain had no food and were near to starving. This is characteristic of the fishermen from all ports, and their bravery helped the country to survive through the two world wars. The governments of the day often turned to our fishermen to help them out in some other political matters too!

The conversation switches from one thing to another, and we are all having our say. Trawlers are landing their fish every weekday, and the three-day millionaires, as the fishermen are known, have only a three-day stay at home with their families before they go back to sea to catch more fish and earn more money. The trawler owners want more fish. They want all the fish in the sea. Businesses and jobs of all trades imaginable are created from the fishing industry, and people are working above their expectations day and night. The town is thriving and Hull, Grimsby and Fleetwood and the ports are among the richest councils in the country, and the communities are among the happiest people in the world. The streets of Hull and the town centre are lit up and alive, with pubs, bars, nightclubs and coffee bars and dance halls, and burger and hot dog stalls on every corner and packed with people. All the big-name stars are lined up to come Hull to entertain because there is lots of money being spent seven days a week. And the same is happening in Grimsby and Fleetwood and all the other fishing ports. There are fishermen here who come from everywhere and willing to sail and keep the network going, whatever the ship is like. They will work in any conditions.

The old man says to Dale, if there is any change in the weather, or if anyone starts fishing, give me a call, and he goes down to the chart room, where he sleeps.

The next day the weather subsides and we shoot the trawl. All the trawlers are fishing, but the weather is still borderline and the nets are getting ripped to shreds on the volcanic seabed, and the trip is no holiday. Basically, nothing has changed. You have to watch the sea, watch each other and watch the danger of the job itself. The rough sea and the frost are still present. Can the safety laws ever make the job safe?

Things are just the same but, even so, the tough little 16-year-old deckie learner is always there and sticking it out without complaining, and Ralph is busy cooking the meals. He is applying to sit for his cook's ticket at the Boulevard Nautical School when we get home. The cook on board the Arctic Corsair is the best around, so Ralph is learning from the best. Ralph cooks for Norma and her mam when he is home, and they are delighted and amazed at how he can put a beautiful meal together without any effort, and make home-made bread and hot cakes.

It's February and we are in the grip of the Arctic winter, but even with new safety regulations, our working conditions have not changed much and we still have to watch ourselves. The normal fishing routine is very much still the same as it has always been, with the exceptions.

The old man's experience has found us a tow with no fastenings and no net mending. We are catching fish and the unpredictable Icelandic weather has changed again for the better, and we make the most of every minute. The old man dishes out the rum and we sing in the pounds while we are putting the fish below.

We have finished the trip off with 1,800 kits of fish after fourteen days, catching more than 100 tons of cod and haddock. The owners have called us home for the best market day. We have stowed the trawl alongside and battened down the hatches, and the old man has rung the Arctic Corsair full ahead for home. Ralph is yodelling up to the stars to pass a message to Norma that we're coming home. The sparks says it is fine weather all the way.

Two days later we are steaming along in the North Sea when, wham, an explosion shockwave shakes the ship from stem to stern and the old man comes flying onto the bridge. We are all stood wondering what it is. The sparks contacts the coastguard, who comes back and says they are setting off explosions in an oil exploration programme, or it could have been an aircraft going through the sound barrier. We stay observant for a while to see if there is any damage, but there is none. The explosion greatly disturbs us, and it could scare the fish away from the North Sea and from the near Atlantic and disturb the fish stocks and breeding grounds. Hull trawlers almost exclusively fish distant waters, going after white fish, not fishing in home waters. But it could greatly affect the livelihood of all the British and Scottish fishing ports along the east coast, including Grimsby, which has 80 per cent of its fleet in the North sea. It could also affect the mid-water cat boats named after big cats, and football boats named after football teams fishing the Faroes and at the west side of Scotland, and scores of small wooden fishing boats of every description.

We have reached the River Humber and catch onto the fast incoming tide that carries us down to St Andrew's dockland, and the Arctic Corsair is home once more. We are tied up to the insurance quay, and there are still wreaths and flowers remaining there. There are people out in the wintry morning doing their business, and the St Andrew's dockland looks like a very sad place. The people of Hull and Hessle Road are still in mourning over the loss of the trawlers and their oved ones, and flowers are still being laid on the quay and the Bullnose and all along Hessle Road. Hull is no stranger to tragedy, but it gets harder every time something bad happens. It is mystifying and scary and it leaves you wondering if it will happen again, and who will be next. The fishermen's families live in the constant hope their loved ones will return home safely to them.

# Chapter 13
# What happened to our ships and men?

The people of Hull have always treated trawler losses as being part of the fishing industry. The three Hull trawlers – the St Romanus, Kingston Peridot and the Ross Cleveland – along with fifty-eight crewmen, were lost at sea. It left fifty-eight widows and sixty-six fatherless children. A group of women decided to confront the trawler owners to demand that safety conditions on fishing trawlers be brought in, and a sisterhood was formed between Lilly Bilocca, Christine Jensen, Yvonne Blenkinsop and Mary Dennes, who made their demands directly to the trawler owners. The police took up a position at the dock entrance to try to stop the women from getting onto the dockland, but there were 400 women and children ready to put up a fight, and extra police were called in for support.

The spokesmen for the trawler owners allowed a meeting and Lilly Bilocca, Rose Cooper and Mavis Wilkinson acted as spokeswomen, because two of the ladies had lost their husbands. Three trawlermen were also allowed to attend. The meeting lasted for fifty minutes, but the delegation were not satisfied, even though the owners answered the questions fairly. They declared the meeting unsatisfactory and the women insisted on a meeting with the owners of the lost trawlers. The owners refused to meet the delegation at that time because they thought it would serve no purpose.

The delegation told the people of the owners' decision not to meet until a later date and the people became angry. The four ladies decided to take things further. They arranged a meeting in London the following Tuesday to lobby the minister of state responsible for the fishing industry. Meanwhile, they visited St Andrew's Dock on each tide to prevent any trawler which was not fully manned from sailing, stressing that the crew must carry a fully, competent wireless operator. They said they would board any trawler that was not fully manned before sailing, and they carried out those threats until the owners of the two missing vessels decided to meet them.

It was impossible to count how many women came to help Lilly and the ladies at these sailings. The next morning there were eight trawlers sailing. The fifth trawler, the St Keverne, a sister ship of the ill-fated St Romanus, came through the lock about 10.20 a.m. The ladies asked the crew if they were fully manned, and one of the crew said, "No, we've no radio operator on board!" Mrs Pye, whose husband was lost on the St Romanus, became hysterical and had to be gently restrained by the police. A policewoman had been instructed to restrain Lilly Bilocca as she tried to board the vessel. She was shouting, "Don't sail short-handed, lads. Don't go." The policewoman made an attempt to prevent Lilly from boarding, but it took another ten police men to hold her until the ship had got through the locks. The St Keverne later returned to the dock to pick up a radio operator.

On the Sunday morning tide, the ladies again attended the lock gates and the only trawler to sail was fully manned. On Monday 5 February, the four ladies met the owners of the two missing vessels. During the talks with the owners, news of the loss of a third Hull trawler, the Ross Cleveland, was just coming through to Hull. Christine Jensen had to withdraw from the meeting because her brother was the skipper of this vessel. One of the owners brought in measures soon to be announced by the government by telling the ladies all his vessels would be banned from the north coast of Iceland during extreme weather.

A point of interest is that Lilly Bilocca and the ladies went to the Houses of Parliament on the 50th anniversary of the Royal Assent being given to the Representation of the People Act (the right for women to vote and stand for parliament).

The public are aware of the four ladies meeting with Mr J.P.W. Mallalieu, Minister of State, Board of Trade, and Mr F. Peart, Minister of Agriculture and Fisheries, and the outstanding success of their endeavours to improve the safety of the fishermen of England.

A deep-sea fisherman's occupation is the most hazardous of all jobs. Statistics show that in the winter at the North Cape of Iceland, fishing is fourteen times more dangerous than a coal miner working in the pit – a worthy comparison. Anything that can be done to alleviate this danger is surely welcome.

On 9 October 1968, the official inquiry into the loss of the three Hull trawlers opened at the City Hall, Hull. The first inquiry was into the loss of the St Romanus. The trawler left Hull on 10 January, and nothing was ever heard of her again. An Icelandic trawler mate told the court that on 11 January, he heard a Mayday call from the St Romanus over his ship's radio. He reported it to his skipper but nothing was done until fourteen days later, when news was received that the St Romanus was presumed lost. On 13 January, an inflatable life raft with the ship's serial number was picked up 265 miles north of Spurn.

The owning company's manager, in evidence, agreed that he should have taken action earlier than 20 January, when he had received no report from the ship. The agreed procedure was that ships would report daily. He did not report to his principals that the St Romanus had not been in contact until 22 January – 12 days after the ship sailed.

A former skipper of the ship put forward a theory that she may have hit a mine, which had been reported in the area roughly where the St Romanus would have been twenty-four hours after leaving Hull.

An inspector gave evidence that the trawler had wireless equipment which was better than that legally required. Radio range, depending on the time of day and position of the ship, could be expected to reach 1,000 miles on high frequency and 150 miles on medium frequency.

Meteorological experts said weather in the area where the ship would be on the 11th was not really bad. There may have been snow showers, and these would cut visibility to 500 yards.

An oceanographer, in a sworn statement, said waves at that time of the year would be an average of 15 feet but could reach 30 feet.

The four Hull ladies attended each day of the hearing and asked to address the court in this first inquiry, but after discussions with Dr Lionel Rosen, representing the Transport and General Workers' Union (TGWU), and some of the relatives, she decided not to pursue her request.

In his closing speech to the court, Mr Barry Sheen, Q.C., Treasury Solicitor, conducting the Board of Trade's case, listed twenty-two questions which he asked the court to answer in an effort to find a possible reason why the trawler was lost. He invited the court to decide that a search was not started promptly enough, and to name any person at fault for this.

The second inquiry, into the loss of the Ross Cleveland, opened with the dramatic evidence of the sole survivor of the disaster, Harry Eddom. He described the hours before the Cleveland sank on 4 February.

He said the crew used axes and battens to get the ice off the ship's sides, and they were kicking the ice off the warp wires. They were kept busy all day, and as fast as they cleared it, more ice formed. During the afternoon, the wind was force eight or nine and it was snowing hard. His skipper, Phil Gay, decided to stow the fishing gear and dodge into shelter. At that time, they were about 33 miles from the coast of Iceland.

Later that day, the wind got up to a force-12 hurricane, and ice on the bridge windows and superstructure on the weather side of the ship was between 3 and 4 inches thick.

As the skipper tried to turn the ship into the wind, it turned over. Mr Eddom was thrown into the icy waters and was later dragged into a life raft by the bosun and another crew member. Both these men died from exposure overnight.

Another skipper sailing in the same area at the same time gave evidence that "the ice, which collected, was the worst I've ever seen". This skipper, Mr Len Whur, was the last to see the Cleveland. He watched on his radar screen, only a quarter of a mile away, as he heard his friend, Phil Gay, appeal over the radio, "Help us, Len. She's going." Mr Whur could do nothing, because to go to the Cleveland's aid would have endangered his own ship, and he had to stand and watch his friend's trawler vanish from the radar screen.

Mr Hlynur Sigtryggsson, of the Icelandic Meteorological Office, described the weather on 4 February as a "storm of hurricane force with 13 degrees of frost, snow falling, the wind was over force twelve accompanied by very heavy seas and spray". He added that the storm, the worst he had seen since 1925, lasted for fifteen hours and was almost unique over three decades.

Another expert described the instability of the Cleveland. If she suffered a severe list of 55 to 60 degrees, she would be in a position where, if the wind continued, she would be unable to get back. In that position, the ventilators would be starting to go under water, the funnel would be taking the sea and the fish in the hold would be likely to move.

In concluding the case for the Board of Trade, Mr Sheen Q.C., invited the court to find that the loss of the trawler was not caused, or contributed to, by the wrongful act of any person or persons. The main thing was to try to find an answer as to how to stop trawlers icing up. Electric element heating of the surface and hot water lances were two of the suggestions mentioned.

Dr Lionel Rosen, for the TGWU, and some of the relatives, criticised the Board of Trade for allowing so much time to elapse between the loss of the Hull trawlers Lorella and Roderigo, thirteen years before (they both capsized with ice) and the present tragedies before acting on the ice problem. He submitted that the time had come for safety legislation to be introduced for trawlers.

Less than 20 tons of ice on her superstructure would have been sufficient to give the Kingston Peridot only a very slender chance of survival in a storm, in one of the theories put forward for the third loss.

On 25 January, the Peridot reported to her owners that fishing was slack on the North Cape of Iceland area and she was steaming eastwards. The next day, the skipper, Ray Wilson, spoke with the skipper of the Kingston Sardius over the radio telephone and told him he was on the north-east corner of Skaggarum and was stowing his fishing gear and steaming eastwards towards the Sardius. It was arranged to contact again at 21.30 hours the next day (27th). No further signals were heard from the Peridot.

Evidence of the weather conditions on 26 January – force-twelve hurricane winds, snow and freezing temperatures – was given to the court.

One theory put forward was that the trawler may have hit a small iceberg, but the vast amount of oil washed up along 70 miles of the Icelandic coast suggested the trawler may have been ripped open on the rocks. The oil, which affected seabirds, was the first sign of the disaster which overtook the trawler when she failed to keep a radio rendezvous with her sister ship.

On 29 January, the day the oil was first sighted, a life raft bearing the name Kingston Peridot was found near Kopasker. Extensive searches for survivors were made but without success. Later the same day three buoys, plus oil and wreckage, were found at Axafjord.

A joint managing director of the owners said in his opinion the ship had not capsized, because her stability was adequate; she had been in similar conditions many times before and he felt if icing up was taking place, a message would have been sent out, and no such message had been received.

In his final summing-up, Mr Sheen Q.C. asked the court to make five recommendations when giving their findings. They were:

(a) All trawler owners should with professional assistance examine the stability of all older vessels;

(b) All owners and the industry should pursue methods of removing ice from trawlers;

(c) Mention the wisdom of restricting areas where fishing took place in vessels of doubtful stability;

(d) Re-emphasise the need to impress on skippers the dangers of icing;

(e) Improve communications between ships and shore.

On Monday 4 November 1968, exactly nine months after Lilly and the ladies of Hull held their original meeting in the Victoria Hall, Mr John Naisby Q.C. announced the findings of the Court of Inquiry.

In the case of the St Romanus, it was not possible to ascertain the cause of her loss. In all probability the ship was lost some time on 11 January in a position not far from where her life raft was found. Mr Naisby made the point that the owners had a system whereby their ships were to report their position daily. He added, "In the opinion of the court, it is no good having a system for the reporting of trawlers unless that system is, in fact, carried out and supervised. There was undue delay in appreciating that something might have happened to the St Romanus, and in the opinion of the court it was time to think seriously on the 12th of the possibility of a casualty."

In fairness to the owners, the court made comment that the weather was by no means exceptional on the 11th and 12th and there was no reason to suppose that, had action been taken on the 12th, anything could have been done to save the ship or the lives of those on board.

There was no excuse for the delay in identification of the life raft, but the court noted that as an interim measure all life rafts in the Hull fleet were now marked "Hull, England".

In giving the court's findings on the other two vessels, the Ross Cleveland and Kingston Peridot, Mr Naisby stated that both were seaworthy in all respects for normal voyages, but hurricane winds with icing conditions and a prolonged period of heavy ice formation meant both lost stability and capsized. He said, "It is indeed fortunate that more vessels were not lost." But in the opinion of the court, these losses clearly demonstrated the need for an investigation into the stability of trawlers in Arctic waters.

An international committee, IMCO, had recommended certain standards of stability. These recommendations included icing conditions which both the Cleveland and Peridot had experienced, and this emphasised that governments may consider a higher standard for their vessels.

# Chapter 14
# Harry tells of his terrible ordeal

The public inquiry into the loss of the Hull trawler Ross Cleveland and the loss of eighteen of her crewmen began at Hull City Hall on 13 November 1968. It was the last time Harry Eddom ever spoke publicly about his ordeal.

During the three-week inquiry, witness testimony evidence was given by Len Whur, skipper of another Hull trawler, Kingston Andalusite, the nearest vessel to the Ross Cleveland at the time of the tragedy.

Whur was desperately trying to save his own ship after being caught in the worst storm experienced off the north-west Icelandic coast in living memory when he received a radio message from his cousin, Phil Gay, skipper of the Ross Cleveland.

The two trawlers were attempting to shelter from the storm in a fjord. Another twenty-eight vessels had also sailed into the fjord hoping to escape from the worst of the weather by seeking a safer anchorage away from the open sea.

At the inquiry, skipper Whur confirmed the chilling words spoken by his cousin seconds before the light on his radar screen indicating the Ross Cleveland's location disappeared.

"I am going over. We are laying over. Help us Len. I am going over. Give my love and the crew's love to the wives and families."

At the time, the wind velocity was measured at 70 knots and the air temperature was recorded at -8°C.

As Gay spoke, first mate Eddom was on deck with two other crew members clearing ice from the radar, which had stopped working after becoming iced up. The protective clothing he was wearing would ultimately save his life.

A sudden lurch of the ship knocked him off balance and sent him flying through the air.

He told the inquiry: "I was jammed against the telegraph and heard a voice saying: 'Come on, we don't want to be here now.'

"We went along the casing after getting through the starboard door of the bridge. They were getting the life raft – the bosun (Walter Hewitt), Barry Rogers and some others. I could not see whether the skipper came out.

"The bosun rolled into the life raft. Rogers had been in the mate's berth."

Eddom said there had been no call from skipper Gay for the crew to get into the life rafts because it had all happened so quickly. "There were only about ten seconds from the ship laying over to sinking."

As he scrambled towards the life raft, a wave crashed into him.

"She threw me into the water. She swilled me to the aft end where they were getting the raft out. I can only surmise the boson and Barry Rogers pulled me in."

Once in the life raft, in the raging sea, Eddom tried to launch a flare and was nearly swept overboard by another huge wave.

The trawler was equipped with three self-inflating life rafts, each one designed to hold up to twelve men. Only three had managed to make it into this one.

"We closed one end of the life raft but the other had got torn and we could not close that," said Eddom. Hewitt took off his boots and started to bail water from the raft to stay afloat as the mechanical bailer had been washed overboard.

While Eddom had donned the usual protective clothing for his ice-breaking duties on deck, which included a shirt, jersey and long johns under a full waterproof oilskin 'duck suit', socks and thigh-high boots, Hewitt and Rogers were not so lucky.

"The bosun had a jersey, a pair of trousers and wellington boots. Barry had a T-shirt and a pair of long johns. I don't think he had any boots," Eddom told the inquiry.

Adrift on the raft, Eddom attempted to protect 18-year-old Rogers from the elements, rubbing his barely-clothed body, while Hewitt continued to use his boots to bail out water. Their efforts would be in vain.

Rogers was the first to die of exposure in the raft within about ninety minutes, followed soon after by 30-year-old Hewitt.

Eddom would drift for the next twelve hours in the raft with the bodies of his crewmates before it was washed ashore on a rocky headland.

"I was awake all the time we were on the raft. I saw nothing more of the Cleveland after we got into the raft," he told the inquiry.

"I had no idea where I was when I came ashore … none at all. I saw a light and just walked around the shore until I got to a farmhouse. There was no one in it.

"I stood behind that until daylight the next morning. I just kept dozing and had no proper sleep. This was when the lad found me. He took me to his farmhouse and then they took me by ship to Isafjord hospital."

His rescuer was the 14-year-old son of a local farmer who had been driving a flock of sheep with his dog.

At the hospital, Eddom was treated for mild frostbite, mainly to his hands and feet. He hadn't been wearing gloves.

Meanwhile, search parties of local Icelanders recovered the bodies of Hewitt and Rogers and two other crew members, trimmer Fred Sawdon and radio operator Rowland Thompson, whose bodies had been washed up in the days following the loss of the trawler. No other crew members were found.

Before being flown back to Britain to be reunited with his wife and young family in Hull, Eddom was required to carry out the grim task of formally identifying the four bodies of his crewmates.

Eleven days after the loss of the Ross Cleveland, the bodies were flown from Reykjavik to Glasgow before three were brought back to Hull by road. The fourth was taken to radio operator Thompson's home town near Aberdeen.

Eddom told the inquiry he had not sailed with Gay before and regarded him as a "very good skipper and a perfect gentleman". He added: "He did everything possible to ensure the maximum safety for the ship and the crew."

Remarkably, Harry Eddom returned to deep-sea fishing three weeks later and would eventually become a trawler skipper, spending the rest of his working life at sea. Like many, when Hull's fishing industry collapsed, he switched to working on support vessels in the oil industry in the Persian Gulf.

In his subsequent report, inquiry chairman Wreck Commissioner Mr John Naisby Q.C. highlighted the issue of emergency clothing supplies for trawler crews in the event of having to abandon a vessel.

He urged trawler firms and insurance companies to ensure that suitable and sufficient clothing was packed into life rafts ahead of any trip to distant-water fishing grounds.

A separate report by eminent physiologist Griffin Pugh on medical aspects of the tragedy concluded that Hewitt and Rogers might have survived had the life raft been fully occupied, with its entrances fully closed.

The Ross Cleveland loss also resulted in the relatively unusual scenario of some families being able to bury their loved ones at home while others were left to mourn those never to return.

Shirley Chatfield is Fred Sawdon's niece. She had taken in two of his five children after their mother died suddenly some years earlier.

"After his wife died, he had to give sea up for a short while because of his children, but he couldn't cope being ashore. His heart was going back to sea," she said.

"His family was taken care of by his sisters-in-law and his niece so he could go back to sea. My mum took the two girls, another auntie took the eldest boy and I took the two youngest boys.

"I looked after them for at least six years up to Fred being lost on the Ross Cleveland, and afterwards I had those two boys until they both grew up and got married.

"When the mission man came to inform us that the ship had gone down with all the crew, it was a shock. Then a few days later the mission man came again to our house and said a body had been washed up on the rocks and they thought it could be Fred.

"We had to identify a name on a tattoo they gave us but I didn't know it. We rang his niece but didn't tell them the name. They knew a tattoo on his arm had the name of a previous girlfriend he used to go out with before he met his wife. That's how they identified him.

"We didn't know what to do, but we had to tell the boys what had happened. Rodney was only 14 and David had just got his first job. The next thing was the big funeral. They are all buried in Hedon Road cemetery.

"His children each got the insurance money but I thought it was a pittance really. They got £100 each – that's what they got for losing their dad. I thought it was disgusting because they couldn't have it until they were 21. They had to be 21 before they could claim it.

"What still upsets me is all those people who have lost loved ones on the trawlers whose bodies haven't come home. We are very lucky because our family member did come home and we have a grave where we can go and tend it.

"Fred would swim home for his family and I think that's what Fred had done. He swam for his life and he was washed up on the rocks. That's the way he came home."

# Chapter 15
# The end of the sidewinders

It's 1972, the years have passed and the face of Hull's fishing industry is changing fast. The Arctic Corsair is still doing very well. She has a new skipper and a new crew now, and the skippers and crews on the trawlers keep changing with the march of time. The Arctic Corsair is still catching a lot of fish and making a lot of money. The sidewinder crews are signing on to the new freezers and factory ships that are replacing the sidewinders. Some of the lads have found jobs in the oil industry on the supply boats. The old man has retired as quite a wealthy man, and you and Steve are working with the Danes on the Seine netters. Dale is the skipper of a supply boat working in the North Sea and Ralph is the cook with him and they are settled. We all still meet for a drink or two when we are home.

It is Christmas Day 1973 and the tragic news has come through that a Hull trawler has been lost. The Ian Fleming sailed through the sacred gates heading for the White Sea in northern Norway, and skipper Dave Arkinson decided to dodge the worst of the weather and cut through the Norwegian fjords. But the ship ran aground at Havoy Sound on Christmas Day 1973. The crew abandoned ship and took to the life rafts, with fifteen men in one raft and five in the other raft that failed to inflate properly, with three men losing their lives. They were three of our very best friends – Terry Day (mate), George Lee (radio operator) and Dennis Coleman (engineer). The skipper and the other crewmen were saved and the survivors and life rafts were rescued later by the Norwegians.

The Ian Fleming stayed on the rocks until the new year, when she sank on 5 January 1974. Incidentally, the 17-year-old deckie learner who survived the tragedy was Jerry Thompson, who is today the president of the Friends of Hull's Fishing Heritage Museum, on Hessle Road, and he has since dedicated his life to the cause. Dave Smith has also dedicated his life to it, alongside Jerry.

Time is moving on fast. Automation and technology are steadily taking over the fishing industry and big freezer trawlers and massive factory ships are being built with the world's latest technology to replace the fresh fish sidewinders. The trawler owners have found the solution to the Iceland weather and icing up. The Iceland mother ship is on location. The cod wars and the fishermen's safety agenda issues are solved. The Hull trawler owners are slick and clever businessmen.

The trawler owners knew from the beginning they could not win the Iceland cod wars, because of the American pressure over Iceland's NATO membership. In the three cod wars, Britain lost hands down in every one of them. In June 1976, the UK and Iceland reached an agreement that has held to this day, and a 200-mile limit is now the standard zone around most countries by international law.

But the cunning minds of the trawler owners wasted no time, and they have brought in modern technology. They have changed the face of the fishing industry, and now the fish merchants are ordering large amounts of frozen fish before it has even been caught. Some of the fish is packed in seven-stone blocks of whole fish that have been frozen almost alive, and they have installed filleting machines and packaging machines on the factory ships, and produce one stone boxes of fillets that will fit straight into your freezer at home, selling them on demand. Every fish is being sold, with no fish is being condemned as unfit. The trawlers have got a free time and motion programme so they can roam the oceans and stay at sea longer, and the fish they catch remains fresher than fresh in the freezer factory until they get home. But at home, jobs are being lost and businesses are closing down and the fishing industry workers begin to feel the pinch, because modern technology and automation are taking their jobs, and the owners are pocketing the profits.

It's still 1973, and Edward Heath has handed the British fishing industry over to the EU. He has sold the fishing communities out and destroyed the fishing network in Hull and Grimsby and in every fishing port in the UK, and the sidewinder trawlers are being laid up and scrapped and sold and businesses of all trades are shutting down. The fishing community workers have nothing left except the dole office; the workforce have been forced out of their jobs and forgotten.

Meanwhile, the Hull trawler owners are doing well for themselves and cashing in on a £100 million decommissioning programme gift that has supposedly been handed over to them. They are pocketing the money that the ships are being sold and scrapped for. They are bringing in millions from the new fleet of new freezer trawlers they are building. And the media have reported on a £15 million gift that was supposedly handed to Edward Heath by the EU that has gone unaccounted for, and the public accused him of lying, while the children of out-of-work fishing men have to wear hand-me-downs because the parents have no money to buy new clothes and shoes for them. It's a shameful, rich-man-poor-man story of power and greed.

It's still 1973 and the Arctic Corsair is back in the headlines yet again under her new skipper, Bernard Whareham. The ship made a trip to the White Sea and filled her holds up with 3,200 kits of cod and haddock, equal to 200 tons of fish, and has broken the world record for weight and money for fresh fish landings.

It's 1974, and we are still trying to cope with the news of the Ian Fleming being lost and the loss of three of our best friends, when the headlines in the *Hull Daily Mail* report the Gaul has not radioed in on her daily schedule. The Gaul left Hull on 22 January 1974. She last reported in on 8 February at 9.30, saying the weather was stormy, with hurricane-force winds, and she reported she was dodging the storm out at the North Cape bank. At 10.30 p.m. that day she failed to answer her daily schedule. On 10 February a message was sent out to all ships to report any contact with the Gaul. The streets of Hull and Hessle Road are waiting for any news of their loved ones, like they have done many times before, and there are thirty-six men on board, leaving behind widows and many fatherless children to add to Hull's trawler disasters.

It's 1975 and St Andrew's Dock is in need of a more modern fish market and more room to manoeuvre because of the expanding fleet of freezer and factory ships. Plans were made to convert the Albert Dock to suit the big trawlers, and a new fish market and landing stage have been built. The Albert Dock has been opened as Hull's new fish dock, and all the trawlers have been diverted there, and St Andrew's Dock is closed. Hull has forty-seven big freezer trawlers and factory ships. It's a big, big fleet.

It's April 1976 and the Arctic Corsair is in the news again. She has a nose for trouble and she is always in the headlines. She has rammed the Odin, the Icelandic protection vessel, and both ships are holed and taking in water. The Odin has staggered into port in Iceland, with serious damage to her stern, and the Arctic Corsair has been patched up and welded on her starboard side again, by the Royal Navy. She is making her way back to Hull for urgent repairs. The Arctic Corsair's skipper, Charlie Pitts, is a character. After the Odin made several attempts to cut the Arctic Corsair's trawl warps, he said: "The Odin is using ambitious and dangerous tactics. I think one is getting too close." That was before he rang the Corsair full ahead, ramming the Odin. It took months to carry out repairs to the Arctic Corsair.

The Arctic Corsair was converted to midwater fishing until 1980, when she was made redundant and laid up in St Andrew's Dock until 1985, when she was changed back to normal fishing and recommissioned to carry on fishing for 100 days, to qualify for a decommissioning grant for the trawler owners. She carried on fishing and beat the UK's gross fresh fish record catch five times over the next two years. In 1988 the owners changed her name from the Arctic Corsair to the Arctic Cavalier, to make way for a new freezer trawler that took over her name.

It's 1990 and the St Andrew's dockland has been shut down for the past fifteen years. It has become accepted in the UK's fishing communities as the

UK's spiritual graveyard in respect to 6,000 lost fishermen and the 900 ships that sailed through the sacred gates and did not come home. There are also thousands of ashes of people that died at home scattered there and the ashes of people who come from everywhere. The fishing communities hold the St Andrew's dockland as sacred, in respect for those who lost their lives at sea. The lost fishermen had no funerals, no coffins, and they have no resting place. Their loved ones go to St Andrew's dockland to pay their respects and find solace.

It's still 1990 and the fishing communities, from everywhere around the UK, are not happy with the way the dock is being disrespected and neglected by the owners of the four remaining buildings, Manor Holdings. The Hull fishermen's group STAND got up a petition for Hull City Council to place a conservation protection order on the east side of the dockland that includes the four remaining buildings, the sacred gates and part of the existing dock. The council and planners had no hesitation in placing a conservation preservation order there, because it's valuable fishing history, and out of respect to Hull's lost fishermen.

In 1993 Adam Fowler, the then leader of the fisherman's group STAND, petitioned for the council to buy the Arctic Cavalier (Arctic Corsair) from the owners for £45,000. They changed her name back to the Arctic Corsair after the council bought her, with the sole intention of berthing her at St Andrew's Dock as a museum ship, along with the sacred gates where she made 232 Arctic expeditions over her twenty-eight years of fishing.

The council bought the Arctic Corsair and planned the necessary arrangements to move her back to St Andrew's dockland, and to create a lost fisherman's memorial park and finally lay the lost souls of the fishermen to rest and bring peace to the city of Hull and to St Andrew's dockland and to the families and friends and fishing communities of the world.

But the owners of the four buildings, Manor Holdings, have different ideas for St Andrew's, regardless of the conservation protection order placed on it.

# Chapter 16
# The resurrection of Babylon

It's 1990, and a preservation order has been placed on the east end of Hull's St Andrew's dockland by Hull City Council, to protect its iconic maritime heritage assets. Also, to protect its status as the spiritual graveyard for 6,000 Hull fishermen and 900 ships lost at sea after sailing through the sacred gates. The lost fishermen did not have a coffin, a funeral, and they have no grave or place to rest. The conservation order was placed there to allow people to pay their respects and find solace for the fishermen who did not come home.

There are two separate owners of the site – Mr John Levison, the new owner of the 11-acre dockland, and Manor Holdings, who own the four remaining buildings. Manor Holdings have put the heritage site up for sale, with plans made to demolish it to make way for a student campus, ignoring its heritage status, and regardless of the conservation protection order and status as a spiritual graveyard and the final place of departure for so many. Also, regardless of the thousands of funeral ashes of the community people that have been scattered there, and even ignoring the Hull planners, who have firmly rejected the campus plans. Manor Holdings have said they plan to build a beautiful campus and accommodation on the site, to house students, to meet their agenda and the needs of the market.

Hull City Council bought the Arctic Corsair, with the intention to berth her at her natural home in St Andrew's Dock, putting her on show as a worldwide tourist attraction. The site has no commercial value, holds a red flag to business people, and it cannot ever be disturbed because it has been recognised by the UK's fishing communities as a sacred spiritual graveyard for lost fishermen. But the owners of the four buildings still have the site up for sale to make way for a student campus, and they refuse to respect the protection order placed on it and the many other reasons the site cannot be disturbed. Now the council have nowhere to berth the Arctic Corsair, so they berth her in the River Hull between the Drypool and Monument Bridges, and they open her for public viewing in 1999.

\*\*\*

It's 1999 and you, Steve, Dale and Ralph have met up for a day out. We meet in Rayners bar, and things have changed dramatically. The pub is quiet, with all the hustle and bustle gone; there are no fishermen and the back room has shut down. There is a crowd of young women with children and babies in their prams sat around the tables at the far end, and a game of bingo starts. We have a pint and decide to go down to look at St Andrew's dockland, then visit the Arctic Corsair. The tunnel entrance is closed to traffic now, so we drive round to St Andrew's Quay, which has been built on the west end of the dockland. The east end sacred gates site is laid bare, and it's a terrible eyesore of vandalism and graffiti. We are shocked. The dock has silted up and water reeds have grown. Only four buildings remain standing, including the Lord Line one, and the sacred gates are in a shocking state.

The sacred gates were the workhorse of Britain's economy, with 350 big Arctic trawlers and each one landing between 100 and 200 tons of fish every three weeks. There was not one single case of a trawler being held back because of bad weather. The trawlers sailed through hell and high water on every tide. It was down to the sea in ships on sailing day, without a word being said.

Dale said it was sacrilege and the owners of the buildings were doing it deliberately to try to destroy the protection order, allowing them to be pulled down. Steve said the company owners of the site were buying properties around the country and leaving them for years to be vandalised, the same as they are doing here. Ralph said the owners have trashed the site's protection order, and told the leaders of the fisherman's Bullnose group – Jerry Thompson, Dave Smith and ex-leader Ray Coles (now retired) – that they are trespassing. They have put up a seven-feet-high fence at the Bullnose to stop people going there to pay their respects. You say they have caused substantial harm to Hull's image too, because this site can be seen from the road by visitors entering and leaving the city, especially the eyesore Lord Line building. The four of us are upset and feeling angry about the state of the dock land, and you say, "I am going to try to do something about this!"

We have driven into town to High Street to visit the Arctic Corsair after so many years and our nervous channels have started. We can see her berthed there and, as we are approaching her, Steve says, "She's enchanted, and she seems to be watching us." Ralph starts to yodel, "Yo, lo, lo, Laydyeee," and the four of us joined in. The visitors on the quay ask why we are all yodelling, and Ralph begins to tell them the story of his life and times on board the Arctic Corsair in full detail. He has a full audience gasping in amazement at what he was telling them. Ralph told them the Arctic Corsair likes being yodelled at, and as we were looking around, we heard the visitors yodelling.

We stay with the Arctic Corsair for two hours and notice how well she has been looked after by the council and the STAND volunteers. We recall the memories and look at our berths and the bunks where we slept and the galley where Ralph worked and the bridge and the foredeck where we risked our lives many times. The memories come flooding back.

It's time for us to leave and we thank the crew who showed us round and say goodbye to the visitors (Ralph's audience). As we leave, Ralph sings out his compelling yodel, to the delight of the yodelling visitors. The Arctic Corsair watches as we leave, and we give her our final wave.

It's 2017, Hull's year as UK City of Culture. The owners of the four iconic buildings still have the sacred gates site up for sale and refuse to budge. Hull City Council and the fishermen's group STAND and the army of valued volunteers have worked over and above their expectations to try to preserve the Arctic Corsair, and a lot of work has been done. Every one of these people deserve a very big thank you; without their efforts the Arctic Corsair would not have survived being laid up all these years. A new berth might have been found in a Ruscador shipyard, which is not the ideal place to berth the world's most famous trawler, but it is the only suitable place the council and planners can find.

It's 2023 and an ex-Hull fisherman, who visited the sacred gates, told Hull City Council how wrong it is for the final place of departure for his lost friends and 6,000 other fishermen to be left in such a vandalised state, even though there is a protection order placed on it, allowing people to visit to pay their respects. The ex-fisherman started a petition to try to retrieve and restore the St Andrew's dockland and create a fisherman's memorial park, with bars, cafes and a play area for the children, as a tribute to its past glory. The petition soon became popular throughout the community, catching the attention of Mr John Levison, the new owner of 11 acres of the St Andrew's dockland (but not the four buildings). Mr Levison told Hull City Council, and HullLive, that he intended to create a fisherman's memorial park, and present a respectable final resting place for the 6,000 lost Hull fishermen. He said it would help Hull's status, and plans were being laid out for work to begin in 2024. Anyone that knows Mr Levison will tell you that he always does a good job.

It's 2024 and the people of Hull are holding their breath, waiting to see the outcome of Mr Levison's plans for the fishermen's memorial park, which is being strongly backed by Hull City Council. The people are waiting for the reaction of Manor Holdings, who own the four buildings, and who have held progress back on the sacred site for fifty years because they have plans to build a student campus on the land. An ex-Hull fisherman has started a petition to berth the Arctic Corsair back at St Andrew's Dock, and has a thousand signed names from the community backing him.

If the plans for the lost fishermen's park go well, and if the Arctic Corsair can be berthed back on the site, Hull can proudly say it has reclaimed the city's crown jewels after fifty years in limbo, and a huge part of the city will be returned to the city and to Hessle Road.

It is wrong for the owners of the four buildings to think they have no obligation to reroof, weatherproof and restore the four buildings, and present them to the sacred gates fishermen's memorial park as a goodwill gift. It would be compensation for the extreme substantial harm they have caused to the site, and to the community and city of Hull.

Thank you, Mr Levison, for your kindness to the fishing communities from everywhere through your decision to lay our loved ones to rest. Amazing grace.

To be continued!

# The crewmen of the Arctic Corsair

Below are the names of some of the Arctic Corsair's courageous crewmen, who will never be forgotten.

----------------------

A. Stan Arnot. Hal Adams. Shaun Andrews.

B. George Bristow. Peter Broderick. Billy Boyle. Chris Bird. Mick Berg.

Bob Bradrey. Mel Brown. Ian Beal. Laurence Bharrell (snr).

C. Authur Ceighton. Tony Calvert. Petr Carmicheal. Brian Crossley.

David Craft. Terry Clarkson.

D. Mick Dolan. Trevor Dennis.

E. Alan Edwards. Eric Everson. Micheal Edmonds. George Ellis.

F. Alan Forrester. Charles Foratarz. Joe Ferraby. Mike Franklin.

Malcom Franklin. Bob Ferrier.

G. Dennis Greening. Jim Grainger.

H. Brian Hodgeson. Simon Herron. Walter Hudson. Cliff Harrison.

John Hough. Les Huoghton. Alan Humphrey. Stanley James Huntly.

K. Steve Kendall. John Karn. Mike Kelly. Ray Kettley. Les Keyworth.

Dave Kaiser. Paul Kirk.

L. Trevor Littlewood. Arthur Leach. Jimmy Lucas.

M. Trevor Marrit. Terry Magee. Tommy Magee. George William Morrison. Lenny Mcguinness. David Mattews.

N. Wally Nash. Steve Nichalson. Terry Nauls. Henk Niejssel.

Peer Nuttal. T Nuttal. Brian Nelson.

P. Dave Pride. Ken Powrill. Sid Powdrell. George Alfred Paige.

Alf Perkins. Dennis Penrose. Walter Portz. John Proctor.

Eddie Pearson. Johh Porter.

S. Dave Stephenson. Ken Stark. John Scot. Raymond Smirk.

Perter Simon. Alf Spencer. Glen Skelton. Ted Sanders.

T. Dave Tindall. Madison Taylor. Dick Taylor. Glen Taylor.

Terry Thresh.

W. Mally Welburn. Terry Withers (Googie). Shaun Wray. C. Walker. Colin Wainright. Terry Wilde. Bernard Wharam.

# The Norman

In October 1952, The Norman sailed through Hull's sacred gates and up the River Humber (known as 'the river of no return'). She sailed down the North Sea and into the Atlantic and across to Cape Farewell, which is 1,500 miles from Hull, taking her six days to get to where the fishing was good. But The Norman ran aground at the southern tip of Greenland at the Skerries. The Norman sank only yards from the shore. The crew tried to swim the few yards to safety, but only the 16-year-old galley boy made it, with the rest of the crew lost.

A Norwegian trawler picked up the distress call and was quickly on the scene, only to find no sign of The Norman, but they saw the boy sitting on a rock. The Norwegians took him on board and he survived. Later, the doctor's examination revealed the lad was very fat and that had helped to stave off the cold, helping him survive for an hour or so. The strange coincidence is that the ship was called The Norman, and the galley boy was called Norman Spencer. The rock was officially named The Norman Rock, and was added to the list of the Hull sacred gates of St Andrew's.

**Lost hull trawlers:**
**The Laurella and The Roderigo**

It's 26 January 1955 at the North Cape of Iceland 1,200 miles from Hull's sacred gates of St Andrew's. It took three and a half days of steam to get there. The weather was atrocious and the ships were battling against it for three days when the Kingston Garnet sent out a Mayday. A wire had got round her screw and she was unable to manoeuvre.

The Laurella and The Roderigo were sheltering in a safe haven but decided to go back out into a living hell to try to help the Kingston Garnet, but what had been intended as a mission of mercy ended in a disaster that the fishing community will never forget. Hurricane-force winds and mountainous seas and the build-up of ice on the rigging forced the ships deeper in the water and made it impossible to turn round and run out of it, and they had to keep into the wind until the end. At 2.35pm The Laurella reported that she was heeling over and couldn't get back, and then there was radio silence.

At 5.10pm The Roderigo reported heeling over for some minutes before radio silence.

Seven months later, the inquiry cleared both skippers of any blame. The two ships sank within one and a half hours of each other. All hands – forty men and boys – were lost with the ships. The worst part of the tragedy was that the Kingston Garnet freed herself and was heading for shelter when the two ships were lost. Back in Hull, people were weeping in the streets, and services were held at the Bullnose and the sacred gates.

## The St Hubert

It's 26 August 1960. The St Hubert left Hull and she is fishing on the Norwegian coast and is nearly ready to go home. Alan Powdrell, the mate's brother, and Billy Wing, the mate's brother-in-law, are 14-year-old schoolboys on a pleasure trip. When they brought the nets up, there was a mine from World War II. The crew did not think it would still be active, so they stowed it on the port side to be dumped in deep water on the way home. It was 11.45 on 29 August 1960 when a gale blew up and battered the St Hubert. It also battered the mine they had picked up, and it exploded. It blew a massive hole in the port side of the ship and four men were killed, including the skipper and the mate. The Hull trawler the Prince Charles went to their aid and took seventeen survivors, including the two schoolboys, to safety. It took six hours for the St Hubert to sink.

## The Staxton Wyke.

It's 1959. The Humber coastguard received an urgent message that a ship had collided with the Staxton Wyke in thick fog off Flamborough Head, fearing she had sunk. They could hear men shouting from two life rafts but they could not be seen. The Flamborough lifeboat was launched and they were picked up. Five men were missing. It is believed she was struck amidships and sank immediately.

### The Arctic Viking

It's 1961. The Arctic Viking sailed through Hull's sacred gates on her last voyage before being scrapped. She sailed to the Noth Cape of Norway with a crew of twenty men. John Keil, the third hand, was put ashore with head injuries at Hammerfest, and he was back at his home in Hull when the news was declared on 20 October 1961.

The Arctic Viking set off for home from the fishing grounds on 12 October 1961 with 1,500 kits, or 95 tons of fish, aboard. As she was passing Flamborough Head she was steering SSW with a full NNW gale behind her, and twice she severely laid over and the skipper stopped the ship. The engineer trimmed her up from the fuel tanks, but she was hit by two massive waves and took on a list and continued to lie over until she capsized. Dave Cressey was at the wheel and said the funnel and the mast were in the water and him and the mate swam for the life raft that had been launched. They were lucky the ship was afloat upside down for a while before she sank. Five men were lost with her and were picked up by a Polish ship, whose divers found the Arctic Viking in 230 feet of water 19 miles off Flamborough Head. Her telegraph was still rang on full ahead.

**St Celestin**

On 27 May 1956, the St Celestin sank after a collision with the Arctic Viking. No information as to what happened can be found.

**The St Finbarr**

On Christmas Day, twelve crewmen died in an explosion on board the St Finbarr off the coast of Newfoundland. She was under tow by the Orsino when she sank rapidly. News of the disaster plunged Hull into despair as families did not know whether their loved ones had survived, only knowing there were thirteen survivors. It was her thirteenth trip and she had been plagued by electric problems for all of it.

**Also lost were:**

The Ian Fleming
St Romanus
Kingston Peridot
Ross Cleveland
The Gaul
Boston York

# Terms and conditions on board a Hull trawler

1. Good rates of pay depending on how much fish you catch.
2. You will work in the Arctic on a sidewinder trawler on a three-week fishing expedition.
3. You will spend three days at home with your family, then go back to the Arctic for another three weeks.
4. You will spend ten months at sea in the Arctic each year.
5. The trawler owners own everything, and they control everything.
6. A fisherman has the most dangerous job – it is fourteen times more dangerous than coal mining.
7. There are no health and safety regulations.
8. Your family will not be compensated for loss of life.
9. It is an accepted part of a fisherman's occupation to be injured or lost at sea.
10. In the winter months, there will be heavy storm clouds and raging winds.
11. It will be dark all the time.
12. You will not see daylight or sunlight or the moon or stars in January.
13. You will go pale, because of the lack of vitamins A and D through the lack the sunlight.

14. You will work for eighteen hours a day in some atrocious weather.

15. As many as 6,000 fishermen and 900 ships have been lost at sea from Hull alone.

16. Hundreds and thousands of fishermen and ships have been lost at sea.

17. You will work alongside Yorkies, Grimmies, Fleeties, Geordies, Puds, the Scots and the Welsh, along with the toughest men from everywhere.

18. There is radio silence because there are no satnavs and no contact home and no radio signals – there is only the ship's VHF and Morse signals.

19. No one is trained in first aid and there is very little in the medicine chest.

20. If you are ill, there is only co-codamol. We call it the wonder pill because it is supposed to cure everything.

21. If you still feel ill, they will give you a huge medicine glass full of rum and maybe forget it.

22. No one is ever ill aboard a trawler.

23. Nothing is provided free and you have to pay for everything you need, except food.

24. You take your own bed and pillow and blanket with you.

25. The fishermen's stores are owned by the trawler owners, who charge full price and take all the money you owe them before you get paid. Even if it is your last penny, they will take it!

26. You will not wear Arctic clothing because you will get too hot and you need to move freely. Your

warm fisherman's gear under your wet gear and rubber boots and gloves and your back-up mittens and fearnots are fine.

27. Sometimes you will haul and shoot in appalling weather and the ship will roll heavily in the swell.

28. There is banging and bumping and chains clanging and the crew shouting.

29. Sometimes you will get iced up, and you will have to chop the ice off the ship's structure.

30. If you smile, you will not be able to straighten your face again for a while.

31. Every sound and movement tells a story to the fisherman.

32. You will work at full speed for up to eighteen hours a day.

33. You will have to watch yourself all the time.

34. There are no sissies saying they are cold and tired.

35. There is none of that here!

36. And don't be surprised if you lose a finger or two!

37. The disaster movie *The Perfect Storm*, starring Russell Crowe, is a good example of a trawler skipper afraid of losing his job if he does not catch enough fish to satisfy the owners, so he decides to stay out in the storms. He lost the ship with all hands. The movie grossed $328 million worldwide for the producers and movie stars to live a life of luxury, but the poor fishermen paid for it with their lives, and their families got nothing.